LINEAR DATA-SMOOTHING
AND PREDICTION
IN THEORY AND PRACTICE

This book is in the

ADDISON-WESLEY SERIES IN
ELECTRICAL ENGINEERING

———————

DAVID K. CHENG and WILLIAM A. LYNCH
Consulting Editors

LINEAR DATA-SMOOTHING
AND PREDICTION
IN THEORY AND PRACTICE

by

R. B. BLACKMAN

Member of the Technical Staff
Bell Telephone Laboratories, Incorporated

ADDISON-WESLEY PUBLISHING COMPANY, INC.

READING, MASSACHUSETTS · PALO ALTO · LONDON · DALLAS · ATLANTA

To Mary,

    Paul and Carol,

        Andreas and Michael;

and to the memory of

    Dad, Mother, and Ruth.

FOREWORD

Once upon a time, a single human brain could encompass the important parts of all that was known about science, mathematics, and related engineering. The accumulated knowledge was within the capacity of the human brain. Now, of course, our technology has become so vast that no one human being can understand more than an extremely small part.

The very vastness of our present knowledge, relative to the capacity of the human brain, tends to fragment our research and development efforts. One kind of fragmentation is between theory and practice. As important theories become mathematically more sophisticated and more varied, it is increasingly difficult for an engineer to understand their pertinence to his specific hardware. On the other hand, as real systems become more complex and more varied, it is increasingly difficult for a mathematician to appreciate the pertinent constraints and conditions. Another kind of fragmentation is between different but related real systems. As individual systems become more complex, it is increasingly difficult for the engineers working on one system to appreciate all the relations to other systems.

As a result, real systems have sometimes been designed without the benefit of pertinent but difficult theory. On other occasions, different specialized forms of general theories have been devised for different but related applications without a full understanding of the interrelationships. Thus an important kind of present-day technical activity is intermediate between theory and practice. One object is to interpret or translate general or abstract theories in terms which will make them more readily available to engineers concerned with real systems. Another is to unify different but related practical approximations to general theories, which have been developed for different applications.

Linear data-smoothing illustrates very well the situation described above. The highly theoretical part is illustrated by the mathematically sophisticated theories of Wiener and Kolmogorov. The practical applications are illustrated by artillery fire control, missile guidance, and determination of satellite orbits (to name but a very few). Applications are different in detail for analog and digital data-smoothing, for real time data-smoothing and data processing at later times, and for fixed schemes and schemes which vary with time.

Mr. Blackman is a master of this field. He has been concerned with linear data-smoothing and prediction for more than 20 years, with particular interest in refining practical techniques and in relating them to general theory and to each other. Through his work, a number of large systems developed at the Bell Telephone Laboratories have realized more fully the theoretical potentialities of linear data-smoothing and prediction.

Murray Hill, New Jersey   SIDNEY DARLINGTON
December 1964

PREFACE

This book grew out of the author's twenty-four years of almost continuous participation in projects which involved data-smoothing and prediction and out of the notes for a series of lectures which the author delivered at the Flight Simulation Laboratory, Branch of Ordinance, White Sands Proving Ground, New Mexico, at the invitation of Dr. Gunther Hintze, Chief of Flight Simulation, in November 1957.

The emphasis in this book is on practical methods rather than optimum methods. It has been common experience in the practical applications of data-smoothing and prediction methods that each application is usually circumscribed by a unique set of practical constraints, so that a method which was judged to be the most practical for one application was usually not judged to be the most practical for another application. In fact, it has frequently happened that a new method, perhaps new only in the sense that it is a composite of parts of older methods, was developed for a particular application. Thus optimum methods are in general useful only as standards for judging the effectiveness of more practical methods. Fortunately, it has not been difficult to find practical methods which achieve efficiencies of 90 percent or more in terms of output signal to noise power ratio, as compared to optimum methods. These efficiencies are generally adequate in view of the uncertainties in the assumptions upon which optimum methods are usually based.

Chapter 1 begins with a brief review of such more or less well-known principles concerning linear invariant analog transmission networks as are relevant to the remainder of the book. In addition, with regard to linear variable analog schemes and linear invariant and variable discrete schemes, this chapter develops points of view which substantially reduce the necessity of treating these schemes entirely independently of linear invariant analog schemes. Chapters 2 and 3, except the last three sections, are devoted to the development of optimum smoothing for polynomial prediction and to an assessment of the penalties incurred with deviations from optimum prescriptions. The last three sections of Chapter 3 are concerned with optimum smoothing in some special situations in which polynomial prediction is either inappropriate or not required. Chapter 4 is devoted to practical analog approximations and their realization with RC networks and high-gain amplifiers. Chapter 5 describes several methods of digitalizing analog filter transfer functions. These methods were originally employed as temporary expedients, but they are still useful under some circumstances. Chapters 6 and 7 are devoted chiefly to the optimization of discrete smoothing schemes. Chapter 8 describes practical discrete smoothing schemes which were developed in order to minimize the complexity of and the time required for arithmetical operations. The last section describes a method of estimating satellite orbital parameters from radar data, a method which was considered for the Telstar I experiments. Chapter 9 is devoted to variable analog and discrete smoothing schemes. Finally, the book closes with Chapter 10 on the measurement of power spectra, inasmuch as the design of data-smoothing and prediction schemes requires at least an approximate knowledge of the noise power spectrum, if not also of the signal power spectrum when this is appropriate. This chapter is partly a condensation of, and partly supplementary to "The Measurement of Power Spectra" by R. B. Blackman and J. W. Tukey. Sections 10.15 and 10.16 on the design of numerical filters and equalizers are useful for applications other than the preparation of data for power spectrum estimation. The material in Section 10.19 is useful where filtering and subsampling are applicable.

My debt to many of my colleagues is evident from the frequent occurrence of their names in the text as well as in the list of references. I wish specially to thank Drs. H. W. Bode, R. L. Dietzold, and S. Darlington for many opportunities of working in the field of data-smoothing and prediction; Dr. J. W. Tukey, in the estimation of power spectra; Mrs. M. G. Wenslau and Mrs. M. B. Taylor, for secretarial assistance; Mrs. E. Jenkins and her group of young ladies, for excellent typescripts; several colleagues and anonymous reviewers for helpful comments; and my wife, Mary, for help in the final preparations for publication.

Murray Hill, New Jersey   R. B. B.
November 1964

CONTENTS

xi

CHAPTER 10.   MEASUREMENT OF POWER SPECTRA

CHAPTER 1

BASIC PRINCIPLES

1.0 Introduction. The term *data-smoothing* refers to the measures which are introduced into the formulation of a data-processing scheme in order to reduce the effects of observational errors (commonly called *noise*). Since data-smoothing generally has also a mutilative effect on the signal component (i.e. the information content) of the data, it presents a need for careful analysis of each application in order to achieve a good practical compromise between its desirable effects and its undesirable effects. It is not possible to list all of the factors which might be relevant to the analysis of each application, but the following are typical.

(1) The statistical structure (autocorrelation function or power spectrum) of the noise. An approximate knowledge of this is usually sufficient.

(2) The statistical structure of the signal. This is usually of such a nature that its representation, *in toto*, by an autocorrelation function or power spectrum would constitute a very inefficient use of the data, as in the case of a piecewise deterministic signal in which the probability distribution of the length of the pieces is at least approximately known and the average length of the pieces is substantial.

(3) The signal may be at least partly under the control of the data-processing equipment, as in the case of a vehicle which is not only under observation or navigation but is also subject to guidance over all or part of its path.

(4) The ultimate specific purpose of data-processing, such as position prediction or retrodiction, velocity prediction, present velocity estimation, maximum travel range, minimum travel time, fuel economy, interception, circularity of orbit at injection, and so on.

In the determination of the orbital elements of the planets, planetoids, natural satellites, and comets, a form of data-smoothing, called *differential corrections*, has been practiced by astronomers for over a century and a half (Baker and Makemson, 1960; Brouwer and Clemence, 1961). However, for reasons which are now largely obscure, the early (1918–1940?) designers of antiaircraft gun directors and bombsights did not develop any rational methods of data-smoothing. The more recent developments in data-smoothing received their impetus from the mathematical investigations conducted by Kolmogorov and by Wiener at about the same time (1940–1941?). Wiener described the results of his work, first in a report with a restricted circulation (Wiener, 1942) and later in a book (Wiener, 1949). In 1950, Bode and Shannon published a description of Wiener's work, in the language of communications engineers.

1

(See also Bendat, 1958.) Wiener's work will not be described in detail in this book.

The methods of data-smoothing described in this book are, largely, extensions of those described in Blackman, Bode, and Shannon (1948). The development of these methods was started in 1940 from the point of view of *curve-fitting*, described in Chapter 3 of this book, which took no explicit account of the statistical structure of the noise. Essentially the same approach to data-smoothing and prediction may have been started at about the same time, although it does not seem to have been followed as far, by Phillips and Weiss (1944).

This chapter is devoted partly to a brief review of the pertinent results of more or less well-known transmission theory and partly to the development of points of view which will be useful in subsequent chapters.

1.1 Classification of data-processing schemes. Data-processing schemes (analog physical devices or digital computer programs) may be classified in various ways.

(1) They may be classified as *linear* or *nonlinear*, according to whether they obey or do not obey the superposition principle. This principle is that the response due to any linear combination of excitation functions is precisely the same combination of the responses due to each of the component excitation functions acting alone. In practice, all data-processing schemes are nonlinear to some extent. The term linear is applied to those schemes in which, by careful design, the effects of nonlinearity may either be treated as noise or may be neglected altogether. The term nonlinear is applied to those schemes in which nonlinearity is deliberately introduced. Except for the last chapter, the treatment in this book is confined to linear schemes.

(2) Data-processing schemes may be classified as *fixed* (parametrically time-invariant) or *variable* (parametrically time-dependent) according to whether a time-shift of the excitation results simply in an equal time-shift of the response, or in something more complex. Our interest in variable smoothing schemes in connection with stationary random noises is based largely on the practical rather than on the theoretical advantages which they offer in some situations. The unification of the analyses of these two classes of schemes, for purposes of data-smoothing and prediction, depends upon the point of view that the concept of weighting function is more fertile than the concept of impulse response (Section 1.7).

(3) Data-processing schemes may be classified as *continuous* or *discrete* according to whether they operate on data supplied continuously or only at discrete (usually equispaced) values of time. Here the unifying concept is introduced in the last two sections of this chapter.

In accordance with the last two ways of classification, there are four categories of data-processing schemes to be analyzed. It is clearly desirable to unify their treatment as much as possible.

FIXED CONTINUOUS SCHEMES

1.2 Impulse response and weighting function. The *impulse response*, $W(t)$, of a linear fixed continuous scheme is, by definition, the response at time t, due to a unit impulse (unit area, infinitesimal duration) excitation applied at time zero. It follows from the parametric time-invariance of the scheme that the response at time t, due to a unit impulse excitation applied at any time λ, is $W(t - \lambda)$. Now, any excitation function may be regarded as the superposition of a sequence of impulses of strength $E(\lambda) \, d\lambda$, in which λ is the *excitation time*. Hence, it follows from the linearity of the scheme that the response $V(t)$ at *response time* t is

$$V(t) = \int W(t - \lambda)E(\lambda) \, d\lambda. \tag{1-1}$$

In mathematical terminology, the response is the *convolution* of the impulse response with the excitation function.

We will make a practice of omitting the limits of integration whenever the range of integration extends, at least formally, from $-\infty$ to $+\infty$. This is permissible in principle provided that the functions appearing in the integrand are specified at all values of their arguments. In many situations, these specifications may be partially implicit. For example, if we are concerned with the response to an excitation initially applied at $\lambda = 0$, then $E(\lambda)$ must be specified as identically zero for $\lambda < 0$. The lower limit of integration is, therefore, effectively zero or greater than zero, depending on the specification of $W(t - \lambda)$ and the value of t. For *real-time* schemes (those which operate on data as fast as the data are gathered) the response at any time t cannot depend upon the excitation applied at times λ greater (i.e., later) than t, so that $W(t - \lambda) \equiv 0$ for $\lambda > t$. The upper limit of integration is, therefore, effectively t. In theory at least, the response at any time t may also be required to be independent of all of the excitation applied at times $\lambda < t - T$, say. Then, $W(t - \lambda) \equiv 0$ for $\lambda < t - T$, and the lower limit of integration is effectively $t - T$, or greater, depending on the specification of $E(\lambda)$.

An advantage in defining functions of time at all values of time and, correspondingly, in defining functions of frequency at all values of frequency (negative as well as positive, notwithstanding the redundancy) is that use can then be made of the correspondence between multiplication of time functions (as in amplitude modulation) and convolution of their frequency (that is, Fourier) transforms, as well as the correspondence between convolution of time functions (as in linear transmission) and multiplication of their frequency transforms. The expression of a theoretical result as a product or convolution of two or more functions often provides valuable insight into the meaning of the result. (See Blackman and Tukey, 1959, especially pp. 66–82, and Chapter 10 in this book.)

By a change of variable of integration, Eq. (1–1) may be written in the form

$$V(t) = \int W(\tau)E(t - \tau) \, d\tau. \tag{1-2}$$

Thus, the response may also be regarded as a weighted integral of the excitation. The *weighting function* $W(\tau)$ is a function of the variable $\tau = t - \lambda$, which is obviously the *age*, at *response time* t, of the datum applied at *excitation time* $\lambda = t - \tau$. If $\int W(\tau)\, d\tau = 1$, the response may be regarded as a weighted average (*smoothing*, in the terminology used in Blackman and Tukey, 1959) of the excitation. If $\int W(\tau)\, d\tau = A$, a nonzero constant other than 1, there is a change in scale factor, as well as a smoothing, of the excitation. Later, we will meet interpretations of the nature of the response, relative to the excitation, under other restrictions on the weighting function, such as $\int \tau^r W(\tau)\, d\tau \equiv 0$ for $r = 0, \ldots, m - 1$, in Chapter 2.

It is perhaps well to emphasize the fact that the identity of the impulse response and the weighting function depends upon the parametric time-invariance of the scheme. This identity does not hold for a variable scheme. The unification of the analyses of these two classes of schemes, for purposes of data-smoothing and prediction, will depend upon taking the point of view that the weighting function is more important than the impulse response.

For a cascade (in filter terminology, a tandem) combination of two linear fixed continuous schemes with individual impulse responses $W_1(t)$ and $W_2(t)$, the composite impulse response $W(t)$ is, by Eq. (1–1) or (1–2), treating the impulse response of the first scheme as the excitation for the second scheme,

$$W(t) = \int W_2(t - \lambda) W_1(\lambda)\, d\lambda$$
$$= \int W_2(\tau) W_1(t - \tau)\, d\tau, \tag{1–3}$$

from which it readily follows that the order in which the two component schemes operate on the data is immaterial.

1.3 Transfer function. Denoting the Fourier transform of $E(\lambda)$, assuming that it exists, by $S_E(i\omega)$, so that

$$S_E(i\omega) = \int E(\lambda) e^{-i\omega\lambda}\, d\lambda,$$

then we have,

$$E(\lambda) = \frac{1}{2\pi} \int S_E(i\omega) e^{i\omega\lambda}\, d\omega.$$

Substituting this into Eq. (1–2), reversing the order of integration, and letting

$$Y(i\omega) = \int W(\tau) e^{-i\omega\tau}\, d\tau, \tag{1–4}$$

we get

$$V(t) = \frac{1}{2\pi} \int S_V(i\omega) e^{i\omega t}\, d\omega,$$

where

$$S_V(i\omega) = Y(i\omega) S_E(i\omega). \tag{1–5}$$

Thus, the Fourier transform $S_V(i\omega)$ of the response $V(t)$ is the product of the Fourier transform $Y(i\omega)$ of the weighting function $W(\tau)$ and the Fourier transform $S_E(i\omega)$ of the excitation $E(\lambda)$.

From the similarity of Eq. (1–3) to Eq. (1–1) or (1–2), it follows also that the Fourier transform $Y(i\omega)$ of the weighting function $W(\tau)$ of a cascade combination of two linear fixed continuous schemes is the product of the Fourier transform $Y_1(i\omega)$ of the weighting function $W_1(\tau)$ of one of the component schemes and the Fourier transform $Y_2(i\omega)$ of the weighting function $W_2(\tau)$ of the other component scheme; that is

$$Y(i\omega) = Y_1(i\omega)Y_2(i\omega). \tag{1–6}$$

The Fourier transform of a weighting function is called the *transfer function*. Its real and imaginary components occur as the amplitudes of the *inphase* and *quadrature* (leading) components of the steady-state response due to a sinusoidal excitation; that is, with $E(\lambda) = \sin \omega\lambda$ in Eq. (1–2),

$$V(t) = \int W(\tau) \sin \omega(t - \tau)\, d\tau$$

$$= \left(\int W(\tau) \cos \omega\tau\, d\tau \right) \sin \omega t$$

$$+ \left(-\int W(\tau) \sin \omega\tau\, d\tau \right) \sin \left(\omega t + \frac{\pi}{2} \right).$$

The simplicity of Eq. (1–5) compared to Eq. (1–1) or (1–2) and that of Eq. (1–6) compared to Eq. (1–3) underlies the usefulness of transfer functions not only in analysis but also in synthesis.

In some cases, Fourier transforms may have to be defined in terms of the theory of "distributions" (Schwarz, 1950; Papoulis, 1962) or of "generalized functions" (Lighthill, 1958). For example, if

$$V(t) = \frac{d}{dt} E(t),$$

which may be written, in the form of a convolution, as

$$V(t) = \int \delta'(\tau) E(t - \tau)\, d\tau,$$

where $\delta'(\tau)$ is the derivative of the Dirac unit impulse or delta function $\delta(\tau)$, then

$$Y(i\omega) = \int \delta'(\tau) e^{-i\omega\tau}\, d\tau = i\omega.$$

Transfer functions which arise in this way are not realizable on account of the pole at infinite frequency. They usually arise in analysis because of some particular artificial resolution of an operation into two or more parts (typically, differentiations and smoothings). In practice, such an operation can usually be resolved in other ways so that all of its parts are conveniently realizable.

1.4 Stationary random input, power transfer function, and power spectra.
The excitation $E(\lambda)$ will usually contain an unwanted component (usually called noise) which may be regarded as coming from a *random (stochastic) process*. The variance of the contribution of such a component to the response $V(t)$ is naturally of considerable interest. Since we are dealing exclusively with linear schemes (which obey the superposition principle) we may simplify the analysis, without loss of generality, by letting $E(\lambda)$ in Eq. (1–1) or (1–2) stand only for the unwanted component of the excitation.

The notation ave $\{-\}$, var $\{-\}$, and cov $\{-,-\}$ will be used to denote the average, variance, and covariance, taken over the ensemble of random functions which a specific random process can generate. We will assume, throughout, that

(a) $\qquad\qquad$ ave $\{E(\lambda)\} = 0 \qquad$ for all λ,

whence

$$\text{var } \{E(\lambda)\} = \text{ave } \{[E(\lambda)]^2\},$$

and

$$\text{cov } \{E(\lambda_1), E(\lambda_2)\} = \text{ave } \{E(\lambda_1)E(\lambda_2)\};$$

(b) $\qquad\qquad$ var $\{E(\lambda)\}$ is independent of λ; and

(c) $\qquad\qquad$ cov $\{E(\lambda_1), E(\lambda_2)\}$ depends only on $|\lambda_1 - \lambda_2|$.

The source of the noise $E(\lambda)$ with these assumed properties is conventionally called a *wide-sense stationary random process*, but, for brevity, we will call it simply a stationary random process.

Further, unless an explicit statement is made to the contrary, our use of the term "stationary random process" will include the assumption of *ergodicity*, so that averages taken over a single infinitely long sample of the noise are equivalent to averages taken over the ensemble. An example of a stationary random process which is not ergodic will be encountered in Section 3.9.

A more general discussion of stochastic processes is not required for the purposes of this book. However, such a discussion will be found in Bartlett (1955), Grenander and Rosenblatt (1957), Parzen (1962), and many other books.

It follows from the assumed properties of the noise input $E(\lambda)$ that for the noise output $V(t)$ of any linear data-processing scheme

$$\text{ave } \{V(t)\} = 0 \qquad \text{for all } t.$$

However, unless the scheme is fixed (i.e., parametrically time-invariant), var $\{V(t)\}$ may not be independent of t, and cov $\{V(t_1), V(t_2)\}$ may not depend only on $|t_1 - t_2|$.

Assuming a stationary random process and a linear fixed continuous data-processing scheme, we have, by Eq. (1–2),

$$[V(t)]^2 = \iint W(\tau_1)W(\tau_2)E(t - \tau_1)E(t - \tau_2)\, d\tau_1\, d\tau_2.$$

(The product of two or more integrals can always be expressed as a multiple integral by using a different variable of integration for each of the original integrals.) Hence, assuming that integration (with respect to time) and averaging (over the ensemble of random functions) are commutative operations, we have

$$\text{var } \{V(t)\} = \iint W(\tau_1)W(\tau_2)C(\tau_1 - \tau_2) \, d\tau_1 \, d\tau_2, \qquad (1\text{--}7)$$

where

$$C(\tau) = \text{ave } \{E(\lambda)E(\lambda + \tau)\}$$

is, by definition, the *autocovariance* of the random process, for time shift (lag or lead) τ. It should be noted that

$$C(0) = \text{var } \{E(\lambda)\} \qquad (1\text{--}8)$$

and that $C(\tau)$ is an even function of τ. It follows from the latter observation that the Fourier transform of $C(\tau)$,

$$P(f) = \int C(\tau)e^{-i\omega\tau} \, d\tau \qquad (\omega = 2\pi f), \qquad (1\text{--}9)$$

is also given by the cosine transform

$$P(f) = \int C(\tau) \cos \omega\tau \, d\tau$$

$$= 2 \int_0^\infty C(\tau) \cos \omega\tau \, d\tau,$$

which shows that $P(f)$ is real and an even function of f. Substituting the inverse of Eq. (1–9),

$$C(\tau) = \int P(f)e^{i\omega\tau} \, df \qquad (\omega = 2\pi f), \qquad (1\text{--}10)$$

into Eq. (1–7), and noting that

$$\int W(\tau_1)e^{i\omega\tau_1} \, d\tau_1 = Y(-i\omega) = Y^*(i\omega)$$

is simply the conjugate-complex of

$$\int W(\tau_2)e^{-i\omega\tau_2} \, d\tau_2 = Y(i\omega),$$

we get

$$\text{var } \{V(t)\} = \int |Y(i\omega)|^2 P(f) \, df. \qquad (1\text{--}11)$$

The squared modulus of the transfer function $Y(i\omega)$, namely $|Y(i\omega)|^2$, is called the *power transfer function*, and the Fourier transform of the autocovariance $C(\tau)$, namely $P(f)$, is the *power spectrum* of the random process.

It follows from Eq. (1–11) that

$$\text{var } \{E(\lambda)\} = \int P(f)\, df = 2 \int_0^\infty P(f)\, df,$$

so that our definition of power spectrum is *two-sided* in the sense that only half of the total power (variance) is in the range $0 < f < \infty$, the other half being in the range $-\infty < f < 0$. (The power spectrum is expressed as "power per cycle per second" in conformity with Blackman and Tukey, 1959, and Chapter 10 in this book.) It follows from Eq. (1–11) also that $V(t)$ may be regarded as coming from a stationary random process whose *power spectrum* is

$$\hat{P}(f) = |Y(i\omega)|^2 P(f), \tag{1–12}$$

corresponding to the autocovariance

$$\hat{C}(\tau) = \text{ave } \{V(t)V(t+\tau)\}$$
$$= \iint W(\tau_1)W(\tau_2)C(\tau_1 - \tau_2 + \tau)\, d\tau_1\, d\tau_2. \tag{1–13}$$

The simplicity of Eq. (1–11) compared to Eq. (1–7) and that of Eq. (1–12) compared to Eq. (1–13) suggests again that it will usually be simpler to work with frequency functions (transfer functions and power spectra) rather than with time functions (weighting functions and autocovariances).

1.5 Cross-correlation of two outputs from a single stationary random input. If two data-processing schemes operate on the same data, then, so far as unwanted random components are concerned, we have

$$\text{var } \{V_1(t)\} = \int |Y_1(i\omega)|^2 P(f)\, df$$

in the response of one scheme, and

$$\text{var } \{V_2(t)\} = \int |Y_2(i\omega)|^2 P(f)\, df$$

in the response of the other scheme. If the responses of the two schemes are combined linearly, in accordance with, say, the equation

$$V(t) = k_1 V_1(t) + k_2 V_2(t),$$

it will usually be wrong (but, as noted in the next paragraph, not always wrong) to assume that

$$\text{var } \{V(t)\} = k_1^2 \text{ var } \{V_1(t)\} + k_2^2 \text{ var } \{V_2(t)\} \qquad \text{(usually wrong)}.$$

Referring to definitions, we have, correctly,

$$\text{var } \{V(t)\} = \text{ave } \{[k_1 V_1(t) + k_2 V_2(t)]^2\}$$
$$= k_1^2 \text{ var } \{V_1(t)\} + k_2^2 \text{ var } \{V_2(t)\} + 2k_1 k_2 \text{ ave } \{V_1(t)V_2(t)\}.$$

The additional term may be expressed in terms of the transfer functions and the input power spectrum. Since

$$\text{var } \{V(t)\} = \int |k_1 Y_1(i\omega) + k_2 Y_2(i\omega)|^2 P(f) \, df$$

$$= k_1^2 \text{ var } \{V_1(t)\} + k_2^2 \text{ var } \{V_2(t)\}$$

$$+ k_1 k_2 \int [Y_1(i\omega) Y_2^*(i\omega) + Y_1^*(i\omega) Y_2(i\omega)] P(f) \, df,$$

it follows that

$$\text{ave } \{V_1(t) V_2(t)\} = \tfrac{1}{2} \int [Y_1(i\omega) Y_2^*(i\omega) + Y_1^*(i\omega) Y_2(i\omega)] P(f) \, df.$$

This represents the *cross-covariance* of $V_1(t)$ and $V_2(t)$.

We note an important result of the last equation, viz., that ave $\{V_1(t) V_2(t)\} = 0$ if either $V_1(t)$ or $V_2(t)$ is an odd-order derivative of the other, in spite of the fact that $V_1(t)$ and $V_2(t)$ are derived from the same source of random excitation. This result is, of course, to be expected from a transmission point of view. If either $Y_1(i\omega)$ or $Y_2(i\omega)$ is $(i\omega)^m$ times the other, where m is an odd positive integer, the frequency components of $V_1(t)$ and $V_2(t)$ will be in quadrature phase at each frequency.

1.6 One output from two cross-correlated stationary random inputs. A somewhat more complicated situation arises if the data supplied to the two schemes come from different sources, and there is cross-correlation between the unwanted random components of the data from the two sources. For simplicity, let $k_1 = k_2 = 1$, so that

$$V(t) = V_1(t) + V_2(t).$$

Then

$$\text{var } \{V(t)\} = \text{var } \{V_1(t)\} + \text{var } \{V_2(t)\} + 2 \text{ ave } \{V_1(t) V_2(t)\}.$$

So far as the first and second terms on the right-hand side are concerned, we have, from previous results,

$$\text{var } \{V_1(t)\} = \int |Y_1(i\omega)|^2 P_1(f) \, df$$

and

$$\text{var } \{V_2(t)\} = \int |Y_2(i\omega)|^2 P_2(f) \, df.$$

The only novelty in these equations comes from the fact that we are now dealing with two random processes with power spectra $P_1(f)$ and $P_2(f)$. For the third term we have, to begin with,

$$V_1(t) V_2(t) = \iint W_1(\tau_1) W_2(\tau_2) E_1(t - \tau_1) E_2(t - \tau_2) \, d\tau_1 \, d\tau_2,$$

whence

$$\text{ave } \{V_1(t) V_2(t)\} = \iint W_1(\tau_1) W_2(\tau_2) C_{12}(\tau_1 - \tau_2) \, d\tau_1 \, d\tau_2,$$

where

$$C_{12}(\tau) = \text{ave } \{E_1(\lambda) E_2(\lambda + \tau)\}$$

is, by definition, the *cross-covariance* of $E_1(\lambda)$ and $E_2(\lambda)$. It should be noted that $C_{12}(\tau)$ is usually *not* an even function, so that the Fourier transform

$$P_{12}(f) = \int C_{12}(\tau)e^{-i\omega\tau}\,d\tau \qquad (\omega = 2\pi f),$$

called the *cross-spectrum*, is usually complex. Since

$$C_{12}(\tau) = \int P_{12}(f)e^{i\omega\tau}\,df \qquad (\omega = 2\pi f),$$

we readily find, as we found Eq. (1–11) from Eqs. (1–7) and (1–10), that

$$\text{ave } \{V_1(t)V_2(t)\} = \int Y_1^*(i\omega)\,Y_2(i\omega)P_{12}(f)\,df.$$

The right-hand member of this equation is real because each factor in the integrand, being the Fourier transform of a real function of a timelike variable, has an even real part and an odd imaginary part.

Consistent with the definition of $C_{12}(\tau)$

$$C_{21}(\tau) = \text{ave } \{E_2(\lambda)E_1(\lambda + \tau)\},$$

so that, under the assumption of stationarity,

$$C_{21}(\tau) = \text{ave } \{E_1(\lambda)E_2(\lambda - \tau)\}$$
$$= C_{12}(-\tau).$$

Hence,

$$P_{21}(f) = P_{12}(-f) = P_{12}^*(f),$$

and

$$\text{ave } \{V_1(t)V_2(t)\} = \int Y_1(i\omega)\,Y_2^*(i\omega)P_{21}(f)\,df.$$

VARIABLE CONTINUOUS SCHEMES

1.7 Connections with fixed continuous schemes. In the analysis of linear fixed continuous data-processing schemes, the most suitable point to use as a point of departure for the analysis of linear variable continuous data-processing schemes is Eq. (1–2), which we now replace by the more general equation

$$V(t) = \int W(\tau;t)E(t - \tau)\,d\tau. \tag{1–14}$$

At any particular value of response time t, the *weighting function* $W(\tau;t)$ is, as before, a function of the *age* τ, at *response time t*, of the datum received at *excitation time* $\lambda = t - \tau$; but now the functional dependence of $W(\tau;t)$ on τ varies with the value of the response time t (regarded as a parameter).

The *impulse response* $I(t;\lambda)$ at response time t, due to a unit impulse applied at excitation time λ, is possibly useful only as a practical tool to determine the weighting function indirectly. Since

$$V(t) = \int I(t;\lambda)E(\lambda)\,d\lambda$$

$$= \int I(t;t - \tau)E(t - \tau)\,d\tau,$$

it follows that $W(\tau;t) = I(t;\lambda)$ where $\lambda = t - \tau$. Thus, if measured or computed values of the impulse response for equispaced values of t and λ are tabulated as shown in Fig. 1.1, the values of the weighting function for equispaced values of τ and t may be read off systematically.*

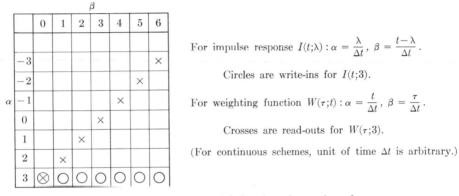

For impulse response $I(t;\lambda): \alpha = \dfrac{\lambda}{\Delta t}$, $\beta = \dfrac{t - \lambda}{\Delta t}$.

Circles are write-ins for $I(t;3)$.

For weighting function $W(\tau;t): \alpha = \dfrac{t}{\Delta t}$, $\beta = \dfrac{\tau}{\Delta t}$.

Crosses are read-outs for $W(\tau;3)$.

(For continuous schemes, unit of time Δt is arbitrary.)

Fig. 1.1. Tabular relation of weighting function to impulse response.

Equation (14) is the basis of an important concept for unifying the analyses, optimization, and design methods for variable and fixed schemes. This equation implies that *for each specific value of response time* t, *there is a fixed scheme which has the same weighting function and therefore yields the same instantaneous value of response as the variable scheme, whatever may be the form of the excitation applied simultaneously to both schemes.* This concept allows us to use the same mathematical techniques for optimizing variable continuous schemes as for fixed continuous schemes. In fact, the results obtained for fixed continuous schemes are directly applicable to variable continuous schemes.

The concept derived from Eq. (1–14) also suggests that the most useful definition of the *transfer function* of a variable continuous scheme is the Fourier transform of the weighting function $W(\tau;t)$ with respect to the *age-of-data* or

---

* The notation used here for the weighting function is more convenient than the one used earlier in Blackman, Bode, and Shannon, 1948. In the earlier notation, the impulse response was denoted by $W(t, \lambda)$, and the weighting function by $W(t, t - \tau)$. Zadeh, 1950a, 1961, uses $h(t, \lambda)$ to denote the response due to an impulse applied at time λ, which corresponds to our earlier notation for the impulse response, presently denoted by $I(t;\lambda)$. Bendat, 1958, uses $h(\tau, t)$ to denote the weighting function presently denoted by $W(\tau;t)$.

time-ago variable τ, regarding the response time t as a constant; that is,

$$Y(i\omega;t) = \int W(\tau;t)e^{-i\omega\tau}\, d\tau. \tag{1-15}$$

In fact, if we substitute

$$E(\lambda) = \frac{1}{2\pi} \int S_E(i\omega)e^{i\omega\lambda}\, d\omega$$

into Eq. (1–14), we get

$$V(t) = \frac{1}{2\pi} \int S_V(i\omega;t)e^{i\omega t}\, d\omega,$$

where

$$S_V(i\omega;t) = Y(i\omega;t)S_E(i\omega). \tag{1-16}$$

This result is nothing more than Eq. (1–5) with only a simple change in notation.

Similarly, all of our results on stationary random processes may be taken over, with only simple changes in notation. For example, Eq. (1–11) now becomes

$$\text{var } \{V(t)\} = \int |Y(i\omega;t)|^2 P(f)\, df, \tag{1-17}$$

which, as we should expect, is now a function of t.

However, we now encounter an essential difference in the composition of the weighting functions and transfer functions of two cascaded schemes. Let

$$V_1(t) = \int W_1(\tau_1;t)E(t - \tau_1)\, d\tau_1$$

be the response of the first scheme, and

$$V(t) = \int W_2(\tau_2;t)V_1(t - \tau_2)\, d\tau_2$$

be the response of the second scheme, so that

$$V(t) = \iint W_1(\tau_1;t - \tau_2)W_2(\tau_2;t)E(t - \tau_1 - \tau_2)\, d\tau_1\, d\tau_2.$$

Substituting $\tau_1 = \tau'$, and $\tau_2 = \tau - \tau'$ (or $\tau_1 = \tau - \tau'$, and $\tau_2 = \tau'$) we get

$$V(t) = \int W(\tau;t)E(t - \tau)\, d\tau,$$

where

$$W(\tau;t) = \int W_1(\tau';t - \tau + \tau')W_2(\tau - \tau';t)\, d\tau'$$

$$= \int W_1(\tau - \tau';t - \tau')W_2(\tau';t)\, d\tau'. \tag{1-18}$$

These equations show that unless the two schemes are equivalent or are invariant, the order in which they operate on the data is *usually* important. (Some exceptions will be noted later.)

As for the transfer function, we have

$$Y(i\omega;t) = \iint W_1(\tau - \tau';t - \tau')W_2(\tau';t)e^{-i\omega\tau}\, d\tau'\, d\tau,$$

which may be integrated with respect to τ, giving

$$Y(i\omega;t) = \int Y_1(i\omega;t - \tau')W_2(\tau';t)e^{-i\omega\tau'}\, d\tau'.$$

Substituting

$$W_2(\tau';t) = \frac{1}{2\pi}\int Y_2(i\omega';t)e^{i\omega'\tau'}\, d\omega', \tag{1-19}$$

we get

$$Y(i\omega;t) = \frac{1}{2\pi}\iint Y_1(i\omega;t - \tau')Y_2(i\omega';t)e^{i(\omega'-\omega)\tau'}\, d\omega'\, d\tau' \tag{1-20}$$

as the general formula for $Y(i\omega;t)$ in terms of $Y_1(i\omega;t)$ and $Y_2(i\omega;t)$.

If the *first* scheme is invariant we can perform the integrations in the right-hand member of Eq. (1–20), first with respect to τ' which now occurs only in the exponential, getting

$$Y(i\omega;t) = Y_1(i\omega)\int Y_2(i\omega';t)\delta(\omega' - \omega)\, d\omega',$$

and then with respect to ω', getting

$$Y(i\omega;t) = Y_1(i\omega)Y_2(i\omega;t). \tag{1-21}$$

Alternatively, we can avoid the δ-function by integrating first with respect to ω', getting

$$Y(i\omega;t) = Y_1(i\omega)\int W_2(\tau';t)e^{-i\omega\tau'}\, d\tau',$$

and then with respect to τ', obtaining Eq. (1–21) as before. If the second scheme is also invariant, then Eq. (1–21) reduces to Eq. (1–6).

If the *first* scheme is an ideal mth order differentiator, then, by Eq. (1–21),

$$Y(i\omega;t) = (i\omega)^m Y_2(i\omega;t).$$

Hence, $Y(i\omega;t)$ is the transfer function of a scheme whose weighting function is

$$W(\tau;t) = \frac{1}{2\pi}\int Y(i\omega;t)e^{i\omega\tau}\, d\omega$$

$$= \frac{\partial^m}{\partial\tau^m}\left[\frac{1}{2\pi}\int Y_2(i\omega;t)e^{i\omega\tau}\, d\omega\right],$$

or, by Eq. (1–19) without the primes,

$$W(\tau;t) = W_2^{(m)}(\tau;t),$$

where

$$W_2^{(m)}(\tau;t) \equiv \frac{\partial^m}{\partial\tau^m}W_2(\tau;t).$$

1.8 Permutable variable continuous schemes. Now, let us consider one of the reasons that the observation made immediately after Eq. (1–18) was qualified by the word "usually." Variable continuous schemes which, under a common transformation of the time variable, satisfy linear differential equations with constant coefficients are permutable. (We will meet their discrete versions in Chapter 9.) For example, the Euler first-order differential equation

$$\left(\frac{t}{k}\frac{d}{dt} + 1\right) V(t) = E(t) \qquad (k > 0,\ t > 0)$$

(see Fig. 1.2) reduces to the differential equation

$$\left(\frac{1}{k}\frac{d}{d\xi} + 1\right) \hat{V}(\xi) = \hat{E}(\xi)$$

under the transformation $\xi = \log t$. Its particular solution is

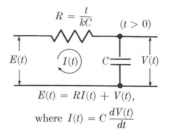

$$R = \frac{t}{kC} \qquad (t > 0)$$

$$E(t) = RI(t) + V(t),$$

$$\text{where } I(t) = C\frac{dV(t)}{dt}$$

FIG. 1.2. A basic circuit for continuous variable smoothing of Euler type.

$$V(t) = \frac{k}{t^k}\int_0^t \lambda^{k-1} E(\lambda)\,d\lambda = \frac{k}{t^k}\int_0^t (t - \tau)^{k-1} E(t - \tau)\,d\tau$$

so that the corresponding weighting function is

$$W_k(\tau;t) = 0 \qquad \text{for } \tau < 0 \text{ and for } \tau > t$$

$$= \frac{k}{t^k}(t - \tau)^{k-1} \qquad \text{for } 0 < \tau < t,$$

including the special case (for $k = 1$)

$$W_1(\tau;t) = 0 \qquad \text{for } \tau < 0 \text{ and for } \tau > t$$

$$= \frac{1}{t} \qquad \text{for } 0 < \tau < t.$$

Such weighting functions are permutable in cascade. A typical cascade combination is that of $W_2(\tau;t)$ and $W_3(\tau;t)$ giving the weighting function

$$W(\tau;t) = 0 \qquad \text{for } \tau < 0 \text{ and for } \tau > t$$

$$= \frac{6}{t^3}\tau(t - \tau) \qquad \text{for } 0 < \tau < t,$$

which may be worked out by Eq. (1–18) or from the Euler second-order differential equation

$$\left(\frac{t}{2}\frac{d}{dt} + 1\right)\left(\frac{t}{3}\frac{d}{dt} + 1\right) V(t) = E(t) \qquad (t > 0).$$

1.9 Fixed schemes treated as variable schemes. Integrating accelerometers.
Following the initial application of excitation to a fixed scheme, there is usually
a more or less well-defined interval of time, called the *settling time*, during which
initial transients contribute appreciably to the response. Alternatively, we
may take the point of view that, during the settling time, the response is
appreciably influenced by false data inasmuch as $E(\lambda) = 0$ for λ less than the
time at which the excitation is initially applied. The settling time may be
defined as the time required by the impulse response to settle to zero, or by the
step response to settle to a constant (which may be zero). If the weighting
function $W(\tau)$ is identically zero for $\tau > T$, as well as for $\tau < 0$, the settling
time is exactly T. Whether the settling time is exactly defined or only approximately defined, the analysis of the response during that time is usually of
interest only from the practical standpoint of scale-factors and of methods of
protection from overload (see Chapter 4). However, a different situation
prevails, for example, in the case of the integrator which plays an essential
role in inertial navigation systems. (An airplane under control of an automatic
pilot behaves like an integrator inasmuch as heading errors generate position
errors across the nominally straight flight path.)

In standard transmission theory, the transfer function of an integrator is
$1/i\omega$. If this is substituted for $Y(i\omega)$ in (1–11), either the integral is divergent,
or the result is unreasonable since it is independent of t. This is because the
transfer function $1/i\omega$ does not take account of the finite length of time during
which integration has been proceeding.

If we imagine the source of excitation and the integrator to be separated by a
switch which is closed at excitation time $\lambda = 0$, it is clear that the impulse
response $I(t;\lambda)$ of the switch-integrator combination must be zero for all pairs
of values of t and λ except those for which $t > \lambda > 0$. The impulse response is
unity for $t > \lambda > 0$. Hence, the weighting function is

$$W(\tau;t) = 1 \quad \text{for } 0 < \tau < t$$
$$= 0 \quad \text{otherwise.}$$

In fact,

$$\int W(\tau;t)E(t - \tau)\, d\tau = \int_0^t E(t - \tau)\, d\tau = \int_0^t E(\lambda)\, d\lambda.$$

Thus, the effective transfer function of an integrator to which excitation is
initially applied at time zero is

$$Y(i\omega;t) = \frac{1 - e^{-i\omega t}}{i\omega}, \qquad t > 0.$$

For a stationary random excitation, by Eq. (1–17),

$$\text{var } \{V(t)\} = \int \frac{2}{\omega^2} (1 - \cos \omega t)P(f)\, df, \qquad \omega = 2\pi f.$$

Thus, if
$$P(f) = \frac{2\sigma^2}{\omega_c} \frac{1}{1 + (\omega/\omega_c)^2},$$

then, for $t > 0$,
$$\text{var } \{V(t)\} = \frac{2\sigma^2}{\omega_c^2} (e^{-\omega_c t} + \omega_c t - 1).$$

If
$$P(f) = \frac{\pi\sigma^2}{\omega_c} \qquad \text{for } |\omega| < \omega_c$$
$$= 0 \qquad \text{for } |\omega| > \omega_c,$$

then, for $t > 0$,
$$\text{var } \{V(t)\} = \frac{2\sigma^2}{\omega_c^2} (\omega_c t \cdot \text{Si } \omega_c t + \cos \omega_c t - 1),$$

where "Si" stands for the "sine-integral" function,
$$\text{Si } x = \int_0^x \frac{\sin u}{u} \, du.$$

Similarly, the weighting function of a double integrator to which excitation is initially applied at time zero is
$$W(\tau;t) = \tau \qquad \text{for } 0 < \tau < t$$
$$= 0 \qquad \text{otherwise},$$

and the effective transfer function is
$$Y(i\omega;t) = \frac{1 - (1 + i\omega t)e^{-i\omega t}}{(i\omega)^2}, \qquad t > 0.$$

DISCRETE SCHEMES

1.10 Connections with continuous schemes. Linear discrete schemes, in general, generate an *output time series* $\{v_k\}$ from an *input time series* $\{u_k\}$ in accordance with a *difference equation* of the form

$$v_k = A_{0k}u_k + A_{1k}u_{k-1} + \cdots + A_{rk}u_{k-r} - B_{1k}v_{k-1}$$
$$- B_{2k}v_{k-2} - \cdots - B_{sk}v_{k-s}. \qquad (1\text{-}22)$$

The impulse response is the sequence $\{I_{k;m}\}$ which, for any specific value of m, is the sequence $\{v_k\}$ due to the excitation

$$u_k = 0 \qquad \text{for } k \neq m$$
$$= 1 \qquad \text{for } k = m \qquad (1\text{-}23)$$

under the condition that
$$v_k = 0 \qquad \text{for } k < m.$$

Then, for $k \geq m$,

$$I_{m;m} = A_{0m},$$

$$I_{m+1;m} = A_{1(m+1)} - B_{1(m+1)}A_{0m} = \begin{vmatrix} A_{1(m+1)} & A_{0m} \\ B_{1(m+1)} & 1 \end{vmatrix},$$

$$I_{m+2;m} = A_{2(m+2)} - B_{1(m+2)}[A_{1(m+1)} - B_{1(m+1)}A_{0m}] - B_{2(m+2)}A_{0m},$$

$$= \begin{vmatrix} A_{2(m+2)} & A_{1(m+1)} & A_{0m} \\ B_{1(m+2)} & 1 & 0 \\ B_{2(m+2)} & B_{1(m+1)} & 1 \end{vmatrix},$$

$$I_{m+3;m} = \begin{vmatrix} A_{3(m+3)} & A_{2(m+2)} & A_{1(m+1)} & A_{0m} \\ B_{1(m+3)} & 1 & 0 & 0 \\ B_{2(m+3)} & B_{1(m+2)} & 1 & 0 \\ B_{3(m+3)} & B_{2(m+2)} & B_{1(m+1)} & 1 \end{vmatrix},$$

and so on. (The broken lines show how each determinant is related to the one before it.) The weighting sequence is the sequence $\{W_{j;k}\}$ in which

$$W_{j;k} = I_{k;k-j}. \tag{1-24}$$

Thus,

$$W_{0;k} = A_{0k},$$

$$W_{1;k} = \begin{vmatrix} A_{1k} & A_{0(k-1)} \\ B_{1k} & 1 \end{vmatrix},$$

$$W_{2;k} = \begin{vmatrix} A_{2k} & A_{1(k-1)} & A_{0(k-2)} \\ B_{1k} & 1 & 0 \\ B_{2k} & B_{1(k-1)} & 1 \end{vmatrix},$$

$$W_{3;k} = \begin{vmatrix} A_{3k} & A_{2(k-1)} & A_{1(k-2)} & A_{0(k-3)} \\ B_{1k} & 1 & 0 & 0 \\ B_{2k} & B_{1(k-1)} & 1 & 0 \\ B_{3k} & B_{2(k-1)} & B_{1(k-2)} & 1 \end{vmatrix},$$

and so on.*

The weighting sequence may be computed directly (that is, for consecutive values of j, and arbitrary fixed values of k) by a method which is analogous in principle to the method discovered by Laning and Battin (1955, 1956) for

---

* Note that the subscripts k, m, j in $I_{k;m}$ and $W_{j;k}$ are analogous to t, λ, τ in $I(t;\lambda)$ and $W(\tau;t)$.

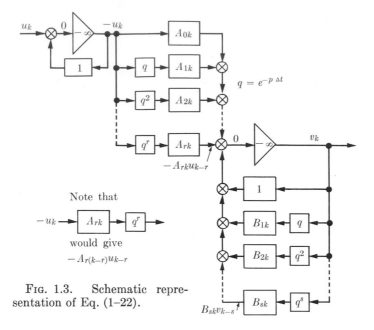

FIG. 1.3.   Schematic representation of Eq. (1–22).

variable continuous weighting functions. Figure 1.3 is a schematic representation of Eq. (1–22). Following Laning and Battin (see Appendix A), Fig. 1.3 is converted to Fig. 1.4 from which we obtain the equation

$$W_{j;k} = A_{0(k-j)}w_j + A_{1(k-j+1)}w_{j-1} + \cdots + A_{r(k-j+r)}w_{j-r},$$

where

$$w_j = D_j - B_{1(k-j+1)}w_{j-1} - B_{2(k-j+2)}w_{j-2} - \cdots - B_{s(k-j+s)}w_{j-s}$$

and

$$D_j = 1 \quad \text{for } j = 0,$$
$$= 0 \quad \text{for } j \neq 0,$$
$$w_j = 0 \quad \text{for } j < 0.$$

In terms of the weighting sequence $\{W_{j;k}\}$, Eq. (1–22) may be expressed in the form

$$v_k = W_{0;k}u_k + W_{1;k}u_{k-1} + W_{2;k}u_{k-2} + \cdots$$

$$= \sum_{j=0}^{\infty} W_{j;k}u_{k-j}. \tag{1–25}$$

This is the discrete version of Eq. (1–14), whereas Eq. (1–22) is the discrete version of the response of the combination of variable continuous schemes shown in Fig. 1.5. We need, therefore, to be cautious in extending the transfer function concept to variable discrete schemes of this generality. Let us consider this point in easy stages.

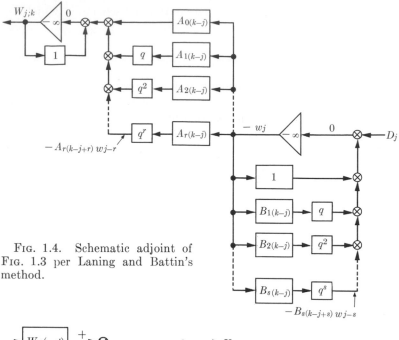

FIG. 1.4. Schematic adjoint of FIG. 1.3 per Laning and Battin's method.

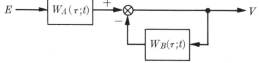

FIG. 1.5. Schematic representation of a recursive (that is, feedback) scheme.

For fixed discrete schemes we may write

$$v_k = A_0 u_k + A_1 u_{k-1} + \cdots + A_r u_{k-r}$$
$$- B_1 v_{k-1} - B_2 v_{k-2} - \cdots - B_s v_{k-s}, \qquad (1\text{--}26)$$

where the A's and B's are independent of k. Let us assume, for the present, that computation is instantaneous (no delay between v_k and u_k for any k), and is perfectly accurate (no roundoff or quantization errors). In all of the applications which we have in mind, the input time series $\{u_k\}$ will have been obtained, in effect if not in fact, by sampling a continuous time function $u(t)$ at uniform intervals Δt of time.* It is clear that the output time series $\{v_k\}$ may also be

---

* Sampling at intervals of Δt has the same effect on the complex amplitude-frequency spectrum of $u(t)$ as the simultaneous double-sideband amplitude-modulation of an infinite set of carrier frequencies spaced uniformly in phase and at intervals of $1/(\Delta t)$ cycles per second. Hence, in order to suppress the degenerative and irreversible effects of *overlapping sidebands* (commonly called *aliasing*, as far as the baseband is concerned), the sampling frequency $1/(\Delta t)$ should be at least twice the highest significant frequency in the spectrum of $u(t)$. (See the reference to Fig. 10.9 in Section 10.8 and the reference to Fig. 10.14 in Section 10.13.)

obtained by sampling the continuous time function $v(t)$ generated from the continuous time function $u(t)$ by a fixed continuous scheme in which

$$v(t) = A_0 u(t) + A_1 u(t - \Delta t) + \cdots + A_r u(t - r \Delta t)$$
$$- B_1 v(t - \Delta t) - B_2 v(t - 2 \Delta t) - \cdots - B_s v(t - s \Delta t). \quad (1\text{-}27)$$

(See Fig. 1.6.) Such a fixed continuous scheme may have the form shown in Fig. 1.5 in which each box is a so-called *transversal filter* (Kallmann, 1940). This continuous scheme has a transfer function of the form*

$$Y(p) = \frac{A_0 + A_1 q + \cdots + A_r q^r}{1 + B_1 q + \cdots + B_s q^s}, \quad (1\text{-}28)$$

where

$$q = e^{-p \Delta t}, \qquad p = i\omega. \quad (1\text{-}29)$$

The series expansion of this transfer function, in powers of q, is

$$Y(p) = W_0 + W_1 q + W_2 q^2 + \cdots,$$

where $W_0, W_1, W_2, \ldots$ are precisely the weights which occur in Eq. (1-25) when Eq. (1-22) is replaced by Eq. (1-26). Hence, we may take Eq. (1-28) as the transfer function of the fixed discrete schemes described by Eq. (1-26).

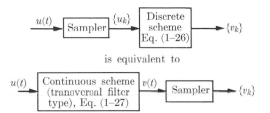

FIG. 1.6. Basic equivalence for treatment of equispaced sampled data obtained from a continuous source.

For variable discrete schemes of *nonrecursive* (that is, nonfeedback) type, characterized by the absence of B-coefficients in Eq. (1-22), we may write

$$v_k = A_{0k} u_k + A_{1k} u_{k-1} + \cdots + A_{rk} u_{k-r}. \quad (1\text{-}30)$$

Hence, we may take

$$Y(p; k \, \Delta t) = A_{0k} + A_{1k} q + \cdots + A_{rk} q^r \quad (1\text{-}31)$$

as the transfer function of variable discrete schemes described by Eq. (1-30).

---

* The numerator is the transfer function of $W_A(\tau; t)$ in Fig. 1.5, while the denominator is the transfer function of $W_B(\tau; t)$.

For variable discrete schemes of *recursive* (that is, feedback) type, characterized by the presence of one or more B-coefficients in Eq. (1–22), we might be tempted to take

$$Y(p;k\,\Delta t) = \frac{A_{0k} + A_{1k}q + \cdots + A_{rk}q^r}{1 + B_{1k}q + \cdots + B_{sk}q^s} \qquad \text{(not valid)} \qquad (1\text{–}32)$$

as the transfer function. The series expansion of this expression, in powers of q, is

$$Y(p;k\,\Delta t) = A_{0k} + \begin{vmatrix} A_{1k} & A_{0k} \\ B_{1k} & 1 \end{vmatrix} q + \begin{vmatrix} A_{2k} & A_{1k} & A_{0k} \\ B_{1k} & 1 & 0 \\ B_{2k} & B_{1k} & 1 \end{vmatrix} q^2 + \cdots$$

The coefficients in this expansion do not agree with the coefficients in Eq. (1–25). Hence, we must conclude that Eq. (1–32) is not valid as an expression of the transfer function. The best we can do is, from Eq. (1–25),

$$Y(p;k\,\Delta t) = \sum_{j=0}^{\infty} W_{j;k}q^j, \qquad (1\text{–}33)$$

which is generally an infinite series.

Regarding $Y(p;k\,\Delta t)$ as an *operator* rather than as a transfer function, we may rewrite Eq. (1–32) in the form

$$Y(p;k\,\Delta t) = Y_2^{-1}(p;k\,\Delta t)\,Y_1(p;k\,\Delta t), \qquad (1\text{–}34)$$

where

$$Y_1(p;k\,\Delta t) = A_{0k} + A_{1k}q + \cdots + A_{rk}q^r, \qquad (1\text{–}35)$$

$$Y_2(p;k\,\Delta t) = 1 + B_{1k}q + \cdots + B_{sk}q^s. \qquad (1\text{–}36)$$

The order in which the operators occur in the right-hand member of Eq. (1–34) is important (see Fig. 1.5). In the inversion of the operator $Y_2(p;k\,\Delta t)$, it must be observed that, for example,

$$B_{1k}qB_{1k}q = B_{1k}B_{1(k-1)}q^2.$$

Thus, the inverse of the operator $Y_2(p;k\,\Delta t)$ is

$$Y_2^{-1}(p;k\,\Delta t) = 1 - B_{1k}q + \begin{vmatrix} B_{1k} & 1 \\ B_{2k} & B_{1(k-1)} \end{vmatrix} q^2$$

$$- \begin{vmatrix} B_{1k} & 1 & 0 \\ B_{2k} & B_{1(k-1)} & 1 \\ B_{3k} & B_{2(k-1)} & B_{1(k-2)} \end{vmatrix} q^3 + \cdots$$

In applying this inverse operator to the operator $Y_1(p;k\,\Delta t)$, it must again be observed that, for example,

$$B_{1k}qA_{0k} = B_{1k}A_{0(k-1)}q.$$

Thus, we finally find that Eq. (1–33) is equivalent to Eq. (1–34) in the noncommutative operational interpretation of the latter.

The fact that the transfer function of a variable discrete scheme of recursive type requires a noncommutative operational interpretation, and therefore may not be regarded as an algebraic expression, will be of no consequence to us in this book. We will have no occasion here to consider variable discrete schemes of genuinely recursive type. The variable discrete schemes of recursive type which we will encounter in this book (Chapter 9) are actually reformulated variable discrete schemes of nonrecursive type, reformulated for practical reasons. They will conform to Eq. (1–30) in which the number of terms is finite though variable ($r = k$). Hence, Eq. (1–31) will be applicable to them. As an example, let the difference equation (see Chapter 9) be

$$v_k = A_{0k}u_k - B_{1k}v_{k-1} - B_{2k}v_{k-2},$$

where

$$A_{0k} = \frac{6}{(k+2)(k+3)},$$

$$B_{1k} = -\frac{2k}{k+3},$$

$$B_{2k} = \frac{k(k-1)}{(k+2)(k+3)},$$

with $k \geq 0$. It will be noted that $v_0, v_1, \ldots$ are independent of what might be stored initially as v_{-1} and v_{-2}. Hence, the weighting sequence will consist of, at most, $k + 1$ terms. The table below corresponds to Fig. 1.1 for this example.

α	$\beta = 0$	$\beta = 1$	$\beta = 2$	$\beta = 3$	$\beta = 4$	$\beta = 5$	$\beta = 6$
0	1	$\frac{1}{2}$	$\frac{3}{10}$	$\frac{1}{5}$	$\frac{1}{7}$	$\frac{3}{28}$	$\frac{1}{12}$
1	$\frac{1}{2}$	$\frac{2}{5}$	$\frac{3}{10}$	$\frac{8}{35}$	$\frac{5}{28}$	$\frac{1}{7}$	
2	$\frac{3}{10}$	$\frac{3}{10}$	$\frac{9}{35}$	$\frac{3}{14}$	$\frac{5}{28}$		
3	$\frac{1}{5}$	$\frac{8}{35}$	$\frac{3}{14}$	$\frac{4}{21}$			
4	$\frac{1}{7}$	$\frac{5}{28}$	$\frac{5}{28}$				
5	$\frac{3}{28}$	$\frac{1}{7}$					
6	$\frac{1}{12}$						

For impulse response: $\quad \alpha = \dfrac{\lambda}{\Delta t} \quad$ or $\quad m, \quad \beta = \dfrac{t - \lambda}{\Delta t} \quad$ or $\quad k - m.$

For weighting sequence: $\alpha = \dfrac{t}{\Delta t} \quad$ or $\quad k, \quad \beta = \dfrac{\tau}{\Delta t} \quad$ or $\quad j.$

The impulse response corresponding to any value of $m \geq 0$ (read horizontally as in Fig. 1.1) has an infinite number of nonzero terms. The weighting sequence corresponding to any value of k (read diagonally upward as in Fig. 1.1) has a finite number of nonzero terms, has a sum of 1, is symmetrical about its midpoint, and has constant second differences.

The weighting sequence $\{W_{j;k}\}$ in any case may be represented as a weighting "function" of the form

$$W(\tau;k\,\Delta t) = \sum_j W_{j;k}\delta(\tau - j\,\Delta t).$$

Thus, by Eq. (1–14),

$$v_k = \int W(\tau;k\,\Delta t)u(k\,\Delta t - \tau)\,d\tau$$

$$= \sum_j W_{j;k}u_{k-j},$$

in accordance with Eq. (1–25), while, by Eq. (1–15),

$$Y(p;k\,\Delta t) = \int W(\tau;k\,\Delta t)e^{-p\tau}\,d\tau$$

$$= \sum_j W_{j;k}e^{-jp\Delta t}$$

in accordance with Eq. (1–33).

1.11 Further uses of Fig. 1.6.   The equivalence illustrated in Fig. 1.6 is useful in other ways. Let us assume, as an example, that the discrete scheme is an mth-order *differencer*. Then

$$Y(p) = \left(\frac{1 - e^{-p\Delta t}}{\Delta t}\right)^m.$$

Since we may write this in the form

$$Y(p) = \left(\frac{1 - e^{-p\Delta t}}{p\,\Delta t}\right)^m p^m,$$

it is clear that the corresponding continuous scheme in Fig. 1.6 may be regarded as a cascade combination of an ideal mth-order differentiator and a continuous scheme whose weighting function is

$$W_m(\tau) = \frac{1}{2\pi i}\int_{-i\infty}^{i\infty}\left(\frac{1 - e^{-p\Delta t}}{p\,\Delta t}\right)^m e^{p\tau}\,dp.$$

This weighting function is the m-fold convolution of the weighting function

$$W_1(\tau) = \frac{1}{2\pi i}\int_{-i\infty}^{i\infty}\frac{1 - e^{-p\Delta t}}{p\,\Delta t}e^{p\tau}\,dp$$

$$= 0 \qquad \text{for } \tau < 0, \text{ and for } \tau > \Delta t$$

$$= \frac{1}{\Delta t} \qquad \text{for } 0 < \tau < \Delta t$$

with itself. The weighting function $W_m(\tau)$ covers the interval $0 < \tau < m\,\Delta t$, and consists of m segments of polynomials of $(m - 1)$th degree, joined into a continuous symmetrical curve with continuous derivatives of all orders up to, and including, the $(m - 2)$th order. For $m = 3$, as a specific example, we have

$$
\begin{aligned}
W_3(\tau) &= \frac{\tau^2}{2\,\Delta t^3}, & 0 < \tau < \Delta t \\[2ex]
&= \frac{\tau^2 - 3(\tau - \Delta t)^2}{2\,\Delta t^3}, & \Delta t < \tau < 2\,\Delta t \\[2ex]
&= \frac{\tau^2 - 3(\tau - \Delta t)^2 + 3(\tau - 2\,\Delta t)^2}{2\,\Delta t^3}, & 2\,\Delta t < \tau < 3\,\Delta t.
\end{aligned}
$$

This is continuous and symmetrical about $\tau = 3\,\Delta t/2$.

CHAPTER 2

POLYNOMIAL PREDICTION

The development of a theory of prediction with optimum smoothing depends to a large extent upon the initial knowledge and/or assumptions regarding the characteristics of the *signal* (relevant and wanted) component of the data and the *noise* (irrelevant and unwanted) component of the data. In Kolmogorov (1941) and in Wiener (1942, 1949) the assumptions were that signal and noise came from stationary random (stochastic) processes (see Bode and Shannon, 1950). In Blackman, Bode, and Shannon (1948) the signal was assumed to be piecewise polynomial with Poisson distribution of discontinuities in time. Zadeh and Ragazzini (1950) assumed the signal itself to be a polynomial combined with a stationary random component.

In this section we will develop the basis for a method of prediction under the assumption that a continuously moving section of the signal may be approximated by a polynomial. For notational convenience, the analysis will be formulated for a fixed-continuous scheme. In view of the earlier discussions, however, it is clear that this analysis, with minor (mainly interpretive) modifications, applies also to the other three categories of linear data-processing schemes (variable-continuous, fixed-discrete, and variable-discrete). In fact, it is necessary only to note that Eq. (1–25) may be expressed in the form of Eq. (1–14),

$$v(k\,\Delta t) = \int W(\tau;k\,\Delta t)u(k\,\Delta t - \tau)\,d\tau,$$

where

$$W(\tau;k\,\Delta t) = W_{j;k}\delta(\tau - j\,\Delta t),$$

and δ stands for the Dirac delta-function.

2.1 Constraints on weighting function. Systematic error. Since we are concerned only with linear schemes (which obey the superposition principle) we may assume, for the purposes of this chapter, that $E(t)$ contains no noise. Nevertheless, weighting functions are introduced into the analysis in this chapter in anticipation of the requirements of the analysis in the next chapter, where we will be concerned with minimizing the effect of noise on polynomial prediction. In fact, the analysis here will impose constraints on the form of the weighting functions.

Starting with Eq. (1–2),

$$V(t) = \int W(\tau)E(t - \tau)\,d\tau$$

and substituting the Taylor-series expansion of $E(t - \tau)$, with remainder term,

$$E(t - \tau) = E(t) - \tau E^{(1)}(t) + \frac{\tau^2}{2} E^{(2)}(t) - \cdots + \frac{(-\tau)^n}{n!} E^{(n)}(t) + R_{0n},$$

where, for $\tau \geq 0$,

$$R_{0n} = \frac{(-)^{n+1}}{n!} \int_0^\tau \xi^n E^{(n+1)}(t - \tau + \xi) \, d\xi,$$

we get

$$V(t) = M_0 E(t) - M_1 E^{(1)}(t) + \frac{M_2}{2} E^{(2)}(t) - \cdots + (-)^n \frac{M_n}{n!} E^{(n)}(t) + R_{Vn}, \tag{2-1}$$

where

$$M_r = \int \tau^r W(\tau) \, d\tau, \qquad r = 0, 1, 2, \cdots, n, \tag{2-2}$$

and

$$R_{Vn} = \frac{(-)^{n+1}}{n!} \int_0^\infty W(\tau) \int_0^\tau \xi^n E^{(n+1)}(t - \tau + \xi) \, d\xi \, d\tau. \tag{2-3}$$

The quantity M_r defined by Eq. (2–2) is the *rth moment of the weighting function*.

The remainder term R_{Vn} defined by Eq. (1–3) may be expressed more meaningfully as follows:

$$R_{Vn} = \frac{(-)^{n+1}}{n!} \int_0^\infty \xi^n \int_\xi^\infty W(\tau) E^{(n+1)}(t + \xi - \tau) \, d\tau \, d\xi$$

$$= \frac{(-)^{n+1}}{n!} \int_0^\infty \xi^n \int_0^\infty W(\tau' + \xi) E^{(n+1)}(t - \tau') \, d\tau' \, d\xi.$$

Hence,

$$R_{Vn} = \frac{(-)^{n+1}}{n!} \int_0^\infty \widehat{W}(\tau') E^{(n+1)}(t - \tau') \, d\tau', \tag{2-4}$$

where

$$\widehat{W}(\tau') = \int_0^\infty \xi^n W(\xi + \tau') \, d\xi. \tag{2-5}$$

Thus,

$$|R_{Vn}| \leq \frac{1}{n!} |E^{(n+1)}|_{\max} \int_0^\infty |\widehat{W}(\tau')| \, d\tau'. \tag{2-6}$$

Note that, by Eq. (1–5), if $W(\tau) = 0$ outside of the interval $0 \leq \tau \leq T$, then, $\widehat{W}(\tau') = 0$ for $\tau' > T$. By Eq. (1–4) or (1–6), we do not need $\widehat{W}(\tau')$ for $\tau' < 0$.

Let us now consider Eq. (2–1) for a special choice of the M_r's. The purpose of this special choice is *prediction*, in which $V(t)$ is to approximate $E(t + \alpha)$, with $\alpha \geq 0$ as the *prediction time*. This special choice will constitute a set of constraints on the form of the weighting function $W(\tau)$ in accordance with

Eq. (2–2), but it will not completely specify the shape of the weighting function. The complete specification of the weighting function depends upon the shape of the power spectrum of the noise in the data, which will be considered in the next chapter. If the weighting function is constrained to satisfy the equations

$$M_r = (-\alpha)^r, \qquad r = 0, 1, \cdots, n, \tag{2–7}$$

then Eq. (2–1) reduces to

$$V(t) = E(t) + \alpha E^{(1)}(t) + \frac{\alpha^2}{2} E^{(2)}(t) + \cdots + \frac{\alpha^n}{n!} E^{(n)}(t) + R_{Vn}.$$

Since

$$E(t + \alpha) = E(t) + \alpha E^{(1)}(t) + \frac{\alpha^2}{2} E^{(2)}(t) + \cdots + \frac{\alpha^n}{n!} E^{(n)}(t) + R_{En},$$

where, for $\alpha > 0$,

$$R_{En} = \frac{1}{n!} \int_0^\alpha \xi^n E^{(n+1)}(t + \alpha - \xi)\, d\xi,$$

then

$$V(t) = E(t + \alpha) + \Delta R_n, \tag{2–8}$$

where

$$\Delta R_n = R_{Vn} - R_{En}.$$

Hence, for $\alpha \geq 0$,

$$|\Delta R_n| \leq |E^{(n+1)}|_{\max} \left\{ \frac{\alpha^{n+1}}{(n + 1)!} + \frac{1}{n!} \int_0^\infty |\widehat{W}(\tau')| d\tau' \right\}. \tag{2–9}$$

More generally, if the weighting function is constrained to satisfy the equations

$$M_r = 0, \qquad 0 \leq r < m, \qquad m \leq n,$$

$$= \frac{(-)^r r!}{(r - m)!} \alpha^{r-m}, \qquad m \leq r \leq n, \tag{2–10}$$

then

$$V(t) = E^{(m)}(t + \alpha) + \Delta R_{mn}, \tag{2–11}$$

where, for $\alpha \geq 0$,

$$|\Delta R_{mn}| \leq |E^{(n+1)}|_{\max} \left\{ \frac{\alpha^{n-m+1}}{(n - m + 1)!} + \frac{1}{n!} \int_0^\infty |\widehat{W}(\tau')| d\tau' \right\}. \tag{2–12}$$

A data-processing scheme whose weighting function satisfies the constraints (2–10) will be called an *mth-order, nth-degree polynomial predictor* (or *updated polynomial smoother* if $\alpha = 0$). Estimates of so-called *systematic* (or *dynamic*) errors may be based upon Eq. (2–12), or upon a simpler but frequently adequate approximation,

$$|\Delta R_{mn}| \approx |E^{(n+1)}|_{\max} \left\{ \frac{\alpha^{n-m+1}}{(n - m + 1)!} + \frac{|M_{n+1}|}{(n + 1)!} \right\}. \tag{2–13}$$

2.2 Constraints on transfer function. Equation (2–1) suggests that the moments of the weighting function are intimately related to the coefficients in the series expansion of the transfer function $Y(p)$ in powers of p. Thus, since

$$Y(p) = \int W(\tau)e^{-p\tau}\,d\tau$$

and

$$e^{-p\tau} = 1 - \tau p + \frac{\tau^2}{2}p^2 - \cdots + \frac{(-\tau)^n}{n!}p^n + \frac{(-p)^{n+1}}{n!}\int_0^\tau \xi^n e^{-p(\tau-\xi)}\,d\xi,$$

we have

$$Y(p) = M_0 - M_1 p + \frac{M_2}{2}p^2 - \cdots + (-)^n \frac{M_n}{n!}p^n + \frac{(-p)^{n+1}}{n!}\hat{Y}(p),$$

where

$$\hat{Y}(p) = \int \hat{W}(\tau')e^{-p\tau'}\,d\tau'.$$

Hence, Eqs. (2–10) will be satisfied if

$$Y(p) = p^m\left[1 + \alpha p + \frac{\alpha^2}{2}p^2 + \frac{\alpha^3}{3!}p^3 + \cdots + \frac{\alpha^{n-m}}{(n-m)!}p^{n-m}\right]$$

$$+ \frac{(-p)^{n+1}}{n!}\hat{Y}(p). \qquad (2\text{–}14)$$

Thus, any $Y(p)$ is the transfer function of an mth-order, nth-degree predictor if its series expansion in powers of p agrees with the series expansion of $p^m e^{\alpha p}$, term for term, up to and including the terms in p^n. The series expansion of the transfer function $Y(p)$ of an mth-order, nth-degree *updated* (*i.e., delay-corrected*) *polynomial smoother* must consist of p^m followed by terms of degree higher than n.*

An mth-order, nth-degree predictor may be regarded, for purposes of analysis, as a cascade combination of an mth-order ideal differentiator and a zero-order $(n - m)$th-degree predictor.

2.3 Step-by-step synthesis. Noise cross-correlation. In this section we will describe a convenient and useful basis for the design and implementation of an mth-order, nth-degree polynomial predictor.

If we have a set of prescribed transfer functions

$$Y_0(p), pY_1(p), p^2Y_2(p), \ldots, p^nY_n(p),$$

where $Y_r(0) = 1$ for every r, it is quite simple to determine a linear (in filter

---

* This property of a polynomial smoother was independently discovered by D. R. Brillinger. It should be noted that "maximally-flat" (or Butterworth) filters, with power transfer functions of the form $1/[1 + (\omega/\omega_c)^{2n}]$, are *not* updated polynomial smoothers.

terminology, a parallel) combination of them, which will satisfy Eq. (2–14) and which will, therefore, be the transfer function of an mth order, nth degree polynomial predictor. It remains to examine the suitability of such a basis from the standpoint of optimization with respect to noise.

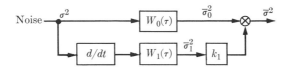

FIG. 2.1. Step-by-step synthesis of a zero-order, first-degree scheme.

In Fig. 2.1, let us assume that, for each $W_r(\tau)$,

(1) $W_r(\tau) \equiv 0$ outside of $0 \leq \tau \leq T$,

(2) $\int W_r(\tau)\, d\tau = 1$ [i.e., $Y_r(0) = 1$],

(3) Aside from the length and area, the shape of $W_r(\tau)$ is optimum in the sense that, for the actual input noise spectrum, the variance $\bar{\sigma}_r^2$ of the noise output of $W_r(\tau)$ cannot be made smaller. We will now show that the noise outputs of $W_0(\tau)$ and $W_1(\tau)$ are not cross-correlated. The weighting function of the whole scheme in Fig. 2.1 is

$$W(\tau) = W_0(\tau) + k_1 \frac{d}{d\tau} W_1(\tau),$$

and the transfer function is

$$Y(p) = Y_0(p) + k_1 p Y_1(p).$$

The length of $W(\tau)$ is obviously the same as the length of $W_0(\tau)$. The area of $W(\tau)$ is the same as the area of $W_0(\tau)$ because $Y(0) = Y_0(0)$. However, the shape of $W(\tau)$ is not the same as the shape of $W_0(\tau)$. Hence, as far as the variance $\bar{\sigma}^2$ of the noise output of the whole scheme is concerned, the presence of the lower branch is equivalent to a change in shape, but not in length or area, of $W_0(\tau)$. It follows, therefore, that $\bar{\sigma}^2$ cannot be less than $\bar{\sigma}_0^2$. Now, let us suppose that

$$\bar{\sigma}^2 = \bar{\sigma}_0^2 + 2\rho k_1 \bar{\sigma}_0 \bar{\sigma}_1 + k_1^2 \bar{\sigma}_1^2,$$

where ρ is the cross-correlation coefficient (for zero lag) between the noise outputs of $W_0(\tau)$ and $W_1(\tau)$. If $\rho \neq 0$, it would be possible to make $\bar{\sigma}^2$ less than $\bar{\sigma}_0^2$ by taking k_1 so that

$$0 < k_1 < -\frac{2\rho\bar{\sigma}_0}{\bar{\sigma}_1} \qquad \text{if } \rho < 0,$$

$$-\frac{2\rho\bar{\sigma}_0}{\bar{\sigma}_1} < k_1 < 0 \qquad \text{if } \rho > 0.$$

We are, therefore, forced to the conclusion that there is no such cross-correlation ($\rho = 0$). Hence,

$$\bar{\sigma}^2 = \bar{\sigma}_0^2 + k_1^2\bar{\sigma}_1^2.$$

To obtain a zero-order, first-degree polynomial predictor with prediction time α, we must take

$$k_1 = \alpha + \int \tau W_0(\tau) \, d\tau.$$

In the optimization of either of the $W_r(\tau)$ with respect to the power spectrum of any stationary random process, subject to constraints only on the length and area, it always turns out that $W_r(\tau)$ is symmetrical about its midpoint (see Chapter 3). This is to be expected on the grounds that an ensemble of stationary random functions may be reversed and/or shifted in time without incurring any change in the autocovariance function or power spectrum. Hence, the first moment of either of the $W_r(\tau)$ is just half of its length. This then raises the question: is it possible to decrease $\bar{\sigma}^2$ by decreasing the length of $W_0(\tau)$, thereby decreasing k_1 for the same α, in spite of the fact that this will necessarily increase $\bar{\sigma}_0^2$, and in spite of (or even perhaps because of) the correlation thus introduced?

To answer this question we may appeal to the straightforward optimization procedure, at least in principle. What we desire, in the end, is a scheme whose overall weighting function $W(\tau)$ is optimized with respect to the noise, subject to constraints on the length, area, and first moment of $W(\tau)$. These constraints are T, 1, and $-\alpha$, respectively. The decreasing of the length of $W_0(\tau)$ in the step-by-step procedure must be reflected as an additional constraint on $W(\tau)$ in the straightforward procedure. This can result only in increasing $\bar{\sigma}^2$.

Hence, the scheme shown in Fig. 2.1 as described above is optimum for any value of the first moment of $W(\tau)$, that is, for any value of k_1.

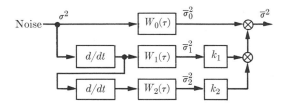

FIG. 2.2. Step-by-step synthesis of a zero-order, second-degree scheme.

Similarly, the scheme shown in Fig. 2.2, with the same conditions imposed on $W_2(\tau)$ as were imposed on $W_0(\tau)$ and $W_1(\tau)$, is optimum for any specific (possibly independent) choice of the values of k_1 and k_2. The variance of the output noise of the whole scheme is

$$\bar{\sigma}^2 = \bar{\sigma}_0^2 + k_1^2\bar{\sigma}_1^2 + k_2^2\bar{\sigma}_2^2. \tag{2-15}$$

To obtain an optimum zero-order, second-degree polynomial predictor with prediction time α, we must take

$$k_1 = \alpha + \int \tau W_0(\tau) \, d\tau \qquad \text{(as before)} \qquad (2\text{--}16)$$

$$k_2 = \frac{\alpha^2}{2} + k_1 \int \tau W_1(\tau) \, d\tau - \frac{1}{2} \int \tau^2 W_0(\tau) \, d\tau. \qquad (2\text{--}17)$$

The scheme shown in Fig. 2.3 is equivalent to that shown in Fig. 2.2, if

$$W_1^{(1)}(\tau) = \frac{d}{d\tau} W_1(\tau),$$

$$W_2^{(2)}(\tau) = \frac{d^2}{d\tau^2} W_2(\tau).$$

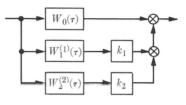

The three parallel branches may also be combined into a single branch with weighting function

$$W(\tau) = W_0(\tau) + k_1 W_1^{(1)}(\tau) + k_2 W_2^{(2)}(\tau).$$

FIG. 2.3.   Equivalent zero-order second-degree scheme.

However, there are many potential and actual practical advantages in blocking out the physical design (implementation) as shown in Fig. 2.3. The physical (usually approximate) realizations of $W_0(\tau)$, $W_1^{(1)}(\tau)$, and $W_2^{(2)}(\tau)$ are independent of the prediction time.* Their outputs are easily combined in various independent ways so that we may have several fixed or continuously variable prediction times simultaneously. Varying the prediction time does not generate additional transients. Further, we may also have optimum first-order, second-degree predictions by combining the outputs of $W_1^{(1)}(\tau)$ and $W_2^{(2)}(\tau)$ through multipliers 1 and k_1', where

$$k_1' = \alpha + \int \tau W_1(\tau) \, d\tau.$$

The optimum smoothed second-order derivative is also available.

This step-by-step development may obviously be generalized to the development of an optimum mth-order, nth-degree polynomial predictor $(m < n)$.

2.4 Analysis of recorded data.

In the post-mortem analysis of recorded data we will not be interested in prediction as such (that is, $\alpha \geq 0$). It is nonetheless necessary to maintain the relations (2–10) among the moments of the weighting function, or, equivalently, the relations among the coefficients in the power-series expansion (2–14) of the transfer function. We may then regard α as another parameter which may be used to minimize the variance $\bar{\sigma}^2$ of the output noise.

---

*In the case of approximate realizations the k-factors must of course be modified to fulfill Eq. (2–14).

It will be in the range $-T < \alpha < 0$, but, as is easily seen, for example, from Eq. (2–15), (2–16), and (2–17), usually not simply $\alpha = -T/2$. In any case, if $\alpha = -\beta$ where $\beta \geq 0$, Eqs. (2–9) and (2–12) are not valid. The remainder term in the power-series expansion of $E^{(m)}(t - \beta)$, after the β^{n-m} term, is

$$\frac{(-)^{n-m+1}}{(n-m)!} \int_0^\beta \zeta^{n-m} E^{(n+1)}(t - \beta + \zeta)\, d\zeta,$$

so that

$$|\Delta R_{mn}| \leq |E^{(n+1)}|_{\max} \left\{ \int_0^\beta \left| \frac{1}{n!} \widehat{W}(\tau') - \frac{(-)^m}{(n-m)!} (\tau')^{n-m} \right| d\tau' \right.$$

$$\left. + \frac{1}{n!} \int_\beta^\infty |\widehat{W}(\tau')|\, d\tau' \right\}. \qquad (2\text{–}18)$$

CHAPTER 3

OPTIMIZATION—CONTINUOUS SCHEMES

3.1 Conditional optimization. In this section we will describe a method of deriving conditionally optimum weighting functions when the noise power spectrum is prescribed as an even rational function. This method will be applied to three related noise power spectra, and in each case we will consider the penalties for using two nonoptimum weighting functions.

Let the power spectrum be

$$\Gamma(\omega) = \frac{M(\omega)}{N(\omega)} \text{ per cycle per second,}$$

where $M(\omega)$ and $N(\omega)$ are even polynomials in ω, of degrees $2m$ and $2n$, respectively. (Here, m and n bear no relation to their meanings in Chapter 2.) Since this power spectrum may be the result of "differentiating" some other power spectrum, as for the inputs to W_1 and W_2 in Figs. 2.1 and 2.2 in the preceding chapter, we put no restriction on the relative values of m and n other than that the original power spectrum, before differentiation, must have finite area. The problem before us is then to determine the weighting function $W(\tau)$, such that

(1) $W(\tau) \equiv 0$ outside of $0 \leq \tau \leq T$,
(2) $\int W(\tau)\, d\tau = 1$,
(3) The shape of $W(\tau)$ in $0 \leq \tau \leq T$ is conditionally optimum in the sense that, with T fixed, the variance of the output noise is a minimum. (The optimum shape will usually depend upon the value of T in such a way that it cannot be expressed as a function of τ/T.)

If $E(t)$ is a typical input noise function, the output noise function is given by

$$V(t) = \int W(\tau)E(t - \tau)\, d\tau.$$

Hence, the variance of the output noise (assuming the average to be zero) is

$$\bar{\sigma}^2 = \text{var } \{V(t)\} = \text{ave } \{[V(t)]^2\}$$

$$= \text{ave }\left\{ \iint W(\tau_1)E(t - \tau_1)W(\tau_2)E(t - \tau_2)\, d\tau_1\, d\tau_2\right\}$$

$$= \iint W(\tau_1)W(\tau_2)C(\tau_1 - \tau_2)\, d\tau_1\, d\tau_2,$$

where

$$C(\tau) = \text{ave } \{E(t)E(t + \tau)\}$$

is, by definition, the autocovariance of the input noise. This equation for $\bar{\sigma}^2$ may also be expressed in the form

$$\bar{\sigma}^2 = \frac{1}{2\pi} \int |Y(i\omega)|^2 P(\omega) \, d\omega,$$

where the transfer function $Y(i\omega)$ and the power spectrum $P(\omega)$ are Fourier transforms of the weighting function $W(\tau)$ and the autocovariance $C(\tau)$, respectively.

The first step in the minimization of $\bar{\sigma}^2$, under the constraints on the length and area of $W(\tau)$, is a problem of very simple type (isoperimetric) in the calculus of variations (see Fox, 1950 or Weinstock, 1952). The result of this step is that $W(\tau)$ must satisfy the integral equation

$$\int C(\xi - \tau) W(\tau) \, d\tau = \hat{k}(\xi), \tag{3-1}$$

where $\hat{k}(\xi)$ is some constant in the interval $0 \le \xi \le T$, but is otherwise determined by the requirement $W(\tau) \equiv 0$ outside of $0 \le \tau \le T$. This integral equation may be solved by expressing it in terms of Fourier transforms,

$$\frac{1}{2\pi} \int P(\omega) Y(i\omega) e^{i\omega\xi} \, d\omega = \hat{k}(\xi) \tag{3-2}$$

and by noting that this equation, in turn, is a solution of the differential equation

$$M\left(-i\frac{d}{d\xi}\right) W(\xi) = N\left(-i\frac{d}{d\xi}\right) \hat{k}(\xi). \tag{3-3}$$

(The last two equations follow immediately from the first if C is regarded as an impulse response, W as the excitation, $\hat{k}$ as the response, P as the transfer function, and Y as the Fourier transform of the excitation W.) Neither of Eqs. (3–2) and (3–3) by itself can give the solution because $\hat{k}(\xi)$ is not prescribed outside of the interval $0 \le \xi \le T$. However, Eq. (3–3) will be used to establish the form which $W(\xi)$ should take in the interval $0 < \xi < T$. The form which $W(\xi)$ should take at $\xi = 0$ and at $\xi = T$ will depend upon whether $m > n$ or $m < n$, as will be seen in due course.

A worthwhile simplification may be based on the fact that $W(\tau)$ will be symmetrical about $\tau = T/2$. This property of $W(\tau)$ follows from Eq. (3–1). Replacing τ by $T - \tau$, and ξ by $T - \xi$, and noting that $C(\tau - \xi) = C(\xi - \tau)$, we get

$$\int C(\xi - \tau) W(T - \tau) \, d\tau = \hat{k}(T - \xi).$$

Subtracting this from Eq. (3–1), we get

$$\int C(\xi - \tau)[W(\tau) - W(T - \tau)] \, d\tau = \hat{k}(\xi) - \hat{k}(T - \xi).$$

Since the right-hand member is zero for any ξ in $0 \leq \xi \leq T$, we must have

$$W(\tau) = W(T - \tau). \tag{3-4}$$

This symmetry is to be expected on the grounds that the autocovariance or power spectrum of a stationary random process is invariant to time reversal and shift.

It is of some interest to note that the transfer function $Y(i\omega)$ corresponding to a weighting function $W(\tau)$ which is symmetrical about some point, say $\tau = a$, must have linear phase. This follows from the fact that the Fourier transform of $W_c(\xi) = W(\xi + a)$, which is symmetrical about $\xi = 0$, must be a real (and even) function, say $A(\omega)$, and therefore

$$Y(i\omega) = A(\omega)e^{-i\omega a}.$$

Thus, the phase characteristic is linear but may be discontinuous at frequencies where $A(\omega)$ is zero.

We may take advantage of the foreordained symmetry of $W(\tau)$ by initially centering it on $\tau = 0$, so that the number of integration constants which we have to carry will be halved. The procedure for determining $W_c(\tau)$ is as follows (Blackman, Bode, and Shannon, 1948):

(1) Formulate the *even* general solution of the differential equation

$$M\left(-i\frac{d}{d\tau}\right)W_c(\tau) = k, \tag{3-5}$$

where k is an unspecified constant over all values of τ. The solution will contain m undetermined constants of integration besides k.

(2) Take the Fourier transform as

$$Y_c(i\omega) = \int_{-T/2}^{T/2} W_c(\tau)e^{-i\omega\tau}\,d\tau, \tag{3-6}$$

thus automatically imposing the condition $W_c(\tau) \equiv 0$ for $|\tau| > T/2$.

It may be noted that, because of the symmetry of $W_c(\tau)$, the function $Y_c(i\omega)$ will be of the form

$$Y_c(i\omega) = F(i\omega)e^{i\omega T/2} + F(-i\omega)e^{-i\omega T/2}. \tag{3-7}$$

(3) Substitute this into

$$\frac{1}{2\pi}\int P(\omega)Y_c(i\omega)e^{i\omega\tau}\,d\omega, \tag{3-8}$$

and integrate (over $-\infty < \omega < \infty$) by the method of residues, for $-T/2 \leq \tau \leq T/2$. The contour of integration must be suitably closed for each term (independently of the other term) of Eq. (3–7).

(4) Impose conditions on the $m + 1$ undetermined constants so that the result of step (3) will be a constant. This constant will be the value of $\hat{k}(\xi)$ in $0 \leq \xi \leq T$, but this value is of no interest or use.

The last step will give n conditions (linear equations) which, together with the normalization of $W_c(\tau)$, are just enough to determine the $m + 1$ constants if $m = n$. But if $m \neq n$ we must supplement the procedure as follows.

If $m > n$ we must find $m - n$ additional conditions to impose, but if $m < n$ we must, somehow, introduce $n - m$ additional undetermined constants before step (2). In either case the supplementary procedure is suggested by the required convergence of

$$\bar{\sigma}^2 = \frac{1}{2\pi} \int P(\omega) |Y_c(i\omega)|^2 \, d\omega. \tag{3-9}$$

If $m > n$, then $Y_c(i\omega)$ must decrease like ω^{n-m-1} as $\omega \to \infty$. Hence, $W_c(\tau)$ and all of its derivatives of order lower than $(m - n)$ must vanish at $|\tau| = T/2$. On the other hand, if $m < n$, then $Y_c(i\omega)$ may increase like ω^{n-m-1} as $\omega \to \infty$. Hence, $W_c(\tau)$ should be supplemented with $n - m$ undetermined constants multiplying the symmetrical "functions"

$$\delta\left(\tau + \frac{T}{2}\right) + \delta\left(\tau - \frac{T}{2}\right),$$

$$\delta'\left(\tau + \frac{T}{2}\right) - \delta'\left(\tau - \frac{T}{2}\right),$$

$$\delta''\left(\tau + \frac{T}{2}\right) + \delta''\left(\tau - \frac{T}{2}\right), \tag{3-10}$$

$$\vdots$$

$$\delta^{(n-m-1)}\left(\tau + \frac{T}{2}\right) + (-)^{n-m-1}\delta^{(n-m-1)}\left(\tau - \frac{T}{2}\right),$$

whose Fourier transforms are, respectively,

$$e^{i\omega T/2} + e^{-i\omega T/2},$$

$$i\omega(e^{i\omega T/2} - e^{-i\omega T/2}),$$

$$(i\omega)^2(e^{i\omega T/2} + e^{-i\omega T/2}), \tag{3-11}$$

$$\vdots$$

$$(i\omega)^{n-m-1}[e^{i\omega T/2} + (-)^{n-m-1}e^{-i\omega T/2}].$$

We will next work out three examples, not only to illustrate this optimization procedure but also to provide material for an assessment of the importance or unimportance of optimum weighting functions in practical applications.

3.2 Example I. Markov noise ($m < n$). In this example, let

$$P(\omega) = \frac{1}{1 + (\omega/\omega_c)^2} \tag{3-12}$$

(so-called Markov noise with autocorrelation function $e^{-\omega_c|\tau|}$). Since $m = 0$,

$n = 1$, let us take

$$W_c(\tau) = k_0 \left[\delta\left(\tau + \frac{T}{2}\right) + \delta\left(\tau - \frac{T}{2}\right) \right] + k_1.$$

Then, by step 2, where the range of integration should include $|\tau| = T/2$,

$$Y_c(p) - \left(k_0 + \frac{k_1}{p}\right) e^{pT/2} + \left(k_0 - \frac{k_1}{p}\right) e^{-pT/2}.$$

Hence, for $-T/2 \leq \tau \leq T/2$, by step 3,

$$\frac{1}{2\pi} \int P(\omega) Y_c(i\omega) e^{i\omega\tau} \, d\omega = k_1 + \left(\frac{k_0 a}{T} - k_1\right) e^{-a/2} \cosh \frac{a\tau}{T},$$

where $a = \omega_c T$. If this is to be a constant, we must take

$$k_1 = \frac{k_0 a}{T}.$$

Then,

$$W_c(\tau) = k_0 \left[\delta\left(\tau + \frac{T}{2}\right) + \delta\left(\tau - \frac{T}{2}\right) + \frac{a}{T} \right]$$

in $-T/2 \leq \tau \leq T/2$. Normalizing, and shifting the origin for τ, we get

$$W(\tau) = \frac{1}{2 + a} \left[\delta(\tau) + \delta(\tau - T) + \frac{a}{T} \right] \tag{3-13}$$

in $0 \leq \tau \leq T$. The corresponding transfer function is

$$Y(p) = \frac{1}{2 + a} \left[\left(1 + \frac{a}{pT}\right) + \left(1 - \frac{a}{pT}\right) e^{-pT} \right].$$

Thus, whereas the variance of the input noise is

$$\sigma_{\text{in}}^2 = \frac{1}{2\pi} \int P(\omega) \, d\omega = \frac{\omega_c}{2}, \tag{3-14}$$

the variance of the output noise is

$$\sigma_{\text{out}}^2 = \frac{1}{2\pi} \int |Y(i\omega)|^2 P(\omega) \, d\omega = \frac{\omega_c}{2 + a}. \tag{3-15}$$

If the optimum weighting function is replaced by

$$\widetilde{W}_\infty(\tau) = \frac{1}{T} \quad \text{in } 0 \leq \tau \leq T \quad (\text{as if } \omega_c \to \infty), \tag{3-16}$$

for which the transfer function is

$$\widetilde{Y}_\infty(p) = \frac{1}{pT} (1 - e^{-pT}),$$

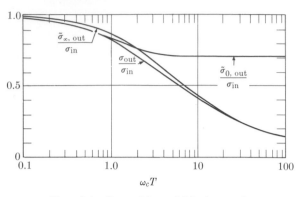

FIG. 3.1. Smoothing of Markov noise.

the variance of the output noise is, with finite ω_c in $P(\omega)$,

$$\tilde{\sigma}_{\infty,\text{out}}^2 = \frac{1}{2\pi} \int |\tilde{Y}_\infty(i\omega)|^2 P(\omega)\, d\omega$$

$$= \frac{\omega_c}{a}\left[1 - \frac{1}{a}(1 - e^{-a})\right]. \qquad (3\text{–}17)$$

On the other hand, if the optimum weighting function is replaced by

$$\tilde{W}_0(\tau) = \tfrac{1}{2}[\delta(\tau) + \delta(\tau - T)] \qquad (\text{as if } \omega_c \to 0), \qquad (3\text{–}18)$$

for which the transfer function is

$$\tilde{Y}_0(p) = \tfrac{1}{2}(1 + e^{-pT}),$$

the variance of the output noise is

$$\tilde{\sigma}_{0,\text{out}}^2 = \frac{1}{2\pi} \int |\tilde{Y}_0(i\omega)|^2 P(\omega)\, d\omega$$

$$= \frac{\omega_c}{4}(1 + e^{-a}). \qquad (3\text{–}19)$$

The ratios $\sigma_{\text{out}}/\sigma_{\text{in}}$, $\tilde{\sigma}_{\infty,\text{out}}/\sigma_{\text{in}}$, and $\tilde{\sigma}_{0,\text{out}}/\sigma_{\text{in}}$ are plotted in Fig. 3.1. The maximum value of $\tilde{\sigma}_{\infty,\text{out}}/\sigma_{\text{out}}$ is approximately 1.07. However, $\tilde{\sigma}_{0,\text{out}}/\sigma_{\text{out}}$ is approximately $(\omega_c T/4)^{1/2}$ for large values of $\omega_c T$.

3.3 Example II. Differentiated Markov noise ($m = n$).

In this example, let

$$P(\omega) = \frac{\omega^2}{1 + (\omega/\omega_c)^2} \qquad (3\text{–}20)$$

(differentiated Markov noise). Since $m = 1$, $n = 1$, let us take

$$W_c(\tau) = k_0 + k_1\tau^2.$$

Then, we find

$$Y_c(p) = \left[\frac{k_0}{p} + k_1\left(\frac{T'^2}{4p} - \frac{T'}{p^2} + \frac{2}{p^3}\right)\right]e^{pT/2}$$

$$- \left[\frac{k_0}{p} + k_1\left(\frac{T^2}{4p} + \frac{T}{p^2} + \frac{2}{p^3}\right)\right]e^{-pT/2}.$$

Hence, for $-T/2 \le \tau \le T/2$,

$$\frac{1}{2\pi}\int P(\omega)\,Y_c(i\omega)e^{i\omega\tau}\,d\omega$$

$$= -\,2k_1 + \left[\frac{k_0 a^2}{T^2} + \frac{k_1}{4}(8 + 4a + a^2)\right]e^{-a/2}\cosh\frac{a\tau}{T},$$

where $a = \omega_c T$. If this is to be a constant, we must take

$$k_1 = -\frac{4k_0}{T^2}\frac{a^2}{8 + 4a + a^2}.$$

Then,

$$W_c(\tau) = k_0\left[1 - \frac{4a^2}{8 + 4a + a^2}\left(\frac{\tau}{T}\right)^2\right]$$

in $-T/2 \le \tau \le T/2$. Normalizing and shifting the origin for τ, we get

$$W(\tau) = \frac{6}{T}\frac{(2 + a) + a^2[(\tau/T)(1 - \tau/T)]}{12 + 6a + a^2} \qquad (3\text{-}21)$$

in $0 \le \tau \le T$. The corresponding transfer function is

$$Y(p) = \frac{6}{12 + 6a + a^2}\left\{\left[\frac{2 + a}{pT} + \frac{a^2}{(pT)^2} - \frac{2a^2}{(pT)^3}\right]\right.$$

$$\left. - \left[\frac{2 + a}{pT} - \frac{a^2}{(pT)^2} - \frac{2a^2}{(pT)^3}\right]e^{-pT}\right\}.$$

Thus, the variance of the output noise is

$$\sigma_{out}^2 = \frac{\omega_c^3}{a}\frac{12}{12 + 6a + a^2}. \qquad (3\text{-}22)$$

If the optimum weighting function is replaced by

$$\tilde{W}_\infty(\tau) = \frac{6}{T^3}[\tau(T - \tau)] \quad \text{in } 0 \le \tau \le T \quad (\text{as if } \omega_c \to \infty), \quad (3\text{-}23)$$

the variance of the output noise is

$$\tilde{\sigma}_{\infty,out}^2 = \frac{12\omega_c^3}{a^3}\left\{1 - \frac{3}{a}\left(1 + \frac{2}{a}\right)\left[\left(1 - \frac{2}{a}\right) + \left(1 + \frac{2}{a}\right)e^{-a}\right]\right\}. \qquad (3\text{-}24)$$

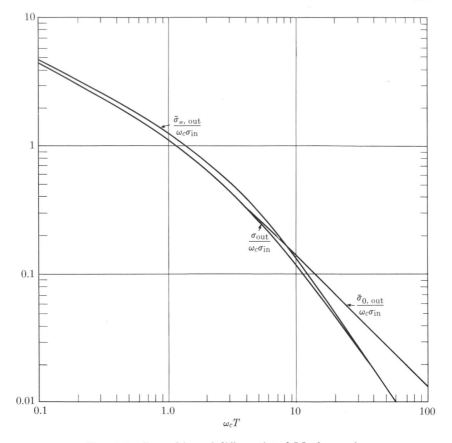

FIG. 3.2. Smoothing of differentiated Markov noise.

On the other hand, if the optimum weighting function is replaced by

$$\widetilde{W}_0(\tau) = \frac{1}{T} \quad \text{in } 0 \le \tau \le T \qquad (as\ if\ \omega_c \to 0), \tag{3-25}$$

the variance of the output noise is

$$\tilde{\sigma}^2_{0,\text{out}} = \frac{\omega_c^3}{a^2}(1 - e^{-a}). \tag{3-26}$$

If the spectrum assumed in this example is the result of actual differentiation of the spectrum assumed in Example I, so that $\sigma^2_{\text{in}} = \omega_c/2$, the dimensionless ratios

$$\sigma_{\text{out}}/\omega_c\sigma_{\text{in}}, \qquad \tilde{\sigma}_{\infty,\text{out}}/\omega_c\sigma_{\text{in}}, \qquad \tilde{\sigma}_{0,\text{out}}/\omega_c\sigma_{\text{in}},$$

are as plotted in Fig. 3.2. The maximum value of $\tilde{\sigma}_{\infty,\text{out}}/\sigma_{\text{out}}$ is approximately 1.10. But $\tilde{\sigma}_{0,\text{out}}/\sigma_{\text{out}}$ is approximately $(\omega_c T/12)^{1/2}$ for large values of $\omega_c T$.

The power spectrum assumed in this example is not realistic because it has infinite area (i.e., variance) and does not correspond to a realistic autocovariance function. However, this situation does not affect the final results, because it is due to the fact that the operation required to obtain the smoothed first derivative of the data is artificially broken down into separate operations of differentiation and smoothing, as shown in Fig. 2.1. A similar situation occurs in the next example.

3.4 Example III. Twice-differentiated Markov noise ($m > n$). In this example, let

$$P(\omega) = \frac{\omega^4}{1 + (\omega/\omega_c)^2},\tag{3-27}$$

(twice-differentiated Markov noise). Since $m = 2$, $n = 1$, let us take now $W_c(\tau) = (T^2 - 4\tau^2)(k_0 + k_1\tau^2)$. Then,

$$Y_c(p) = \left[k_0\left(\frac{4T}{p^2} - \frac{8}{p^3}\right) + k_1\left(\frac{T^3}{p^2} - \frac{10T^2}{p^3} + \frac{48T}{p^4} - \frac{96}{p^5}\right)\right]e^{pT/2}$$

$$+ \left[k_0\left(\frac{4T}{p^2} + \frac{8}{p^3}\right) + k_1\left(\frac{T^3}{p^2} + \frac{10T^2}{p^3} + \frac{48T}{p^4} + \frac{96}{p^5}\right)\right]e^{-pT/2}.$$

Hence, for $-T/2 \leq \tau \leq T/2$,

$$\frac{1}{2\pi}\int P(\omega)\,Y_c(i\omega)e^{i\omega\tau}\,d\omega$$

$$= -\,96k_1 + \left[\frac{4k_0a^2(2+a)}{T^2} + k_1(96 + 48a + 10a^2 + a^3)\right]e^{-a/2}\cosh\frac{a\tau}{T},$$

where $a = \omega_c T$. If this is to be a constant, we must take

$$k_1 = -\,\frac{4k_0}{T^2}\,\frac{a^2(2+a)}{96 + 48a + 10a^2 + a^3}.$$

Then,

$$W_c(\tau) = k_0(T^2 - 4\tau^2)\left[1 - \frac{4a^2(2+a)}{96 + 48a + 10a^2 + a^3}\left(\frac{\tau}{T}\right)^2\right]$$

in $-T/2 \leq \tau \leq T/2$. Normalizing and shifting the origin for τ, we get

$$W(\tau) = \frac{30}{T}\,\frac{2(12 + 6a + a^2)[(\tau/T)(1 - \tau/T)] + a^2(2 + a)[(\tau/T)(1 - \tau/T)]^2}{120 + 60a + 12a^2 + a^3}$$

$$\tag{3-28}$$

in $0 \leq \tau \leq T$. The corresponding transfer function is

$$Y(p) = \frac{60}{120 + 60a + 12a^2 + a^3}$$

$$\times \left\{\left[\frac{12 + 6a + a^2}{(pT)^2} - \frac{24 + 12a - a^3}{(pT)^3} - \frac{6a^2(2+a)}{(pT)^4} + \frac{12a^2(2+a)}{(pT)^5}\right]\right.$$

$$+ \left.\left[\frac{12 + 6a + a^2}{(pT)^2} + \frac{24 + 12a - a^3}{(pT)^3} - \frac{6a^2(2+a)}{(pT)^4} - \frac{12a^2(2+a)}{(pT)^5}\right]e^{-pT}\right\}.$$

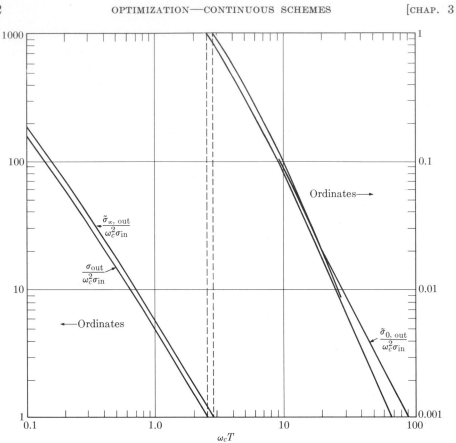

Fig. 3.3. Smoothing of twice-differentiated Markov noise.

Thus, the variance of the output noise is

$$\sigma_{\text{out}}^2 = \frac{\omega_c^5}{a^3} \frac{720(2 + a)}{120 + 60a + 12a^2 + a^3}. \tag{3-29}$$

If the optimum weighting function is replaced by

$$\widetilde{W}_\infty(\tau) = \frac{30}{T^5} [\tau(T - \tau)]^2 \quad \text{in } 0 \leq \tau \leq T \quad (\text{as if } \omega_c \to \infty), \tag{3-30}$$

the variance of the output noise is

$$\tilde{\sigma}_{\infty,\text{out}}^2 = \frac{720\omega_c^5}{a^5} \left\{ 1 - \frac{5}{a}\left(1 + \frac{6}{a} + \frac{12}{a^2}\right)\left[\left(1 - \frac{6}{a} + \frac{12}{a^2}\right)\right.\right.$$
$$\left.\left. - \left(1 + \frac{6}{a} + \frac{12}{a^2}\right)e^{-a}\right]\right\}. \tag{3-31}$$

On the other hand, if the optimum weighting function is replaced by

$$\widetilde{W}_0(\tau) = \frac{6}{T^3}[\tau(T - \tau)] \quad \text{in } 0 \leq \tau \leq T \quad \text{(as if } \omega_c \to 0\text{),} \quad (3\text{-}32)$$

the variance of the output noise is

$$\widetilde{\sigma}_{0,\text{out}}^2 - \frac{36\omega_c^5}{a^4}\left(1 + \frac{2}{a}\right)\left[\left(1 - \frac{2}{a}\right) + \left(1 + \frac{2}{a}\right)e^{-a}\right]. \quad (3\text{-}33)$$

If the spectrum assumed in this example is the result of actual double differentiation of the spectrum assumed in Example I, so that $\sigma_{\text{in}}^2 = \omega_c/2$, the dimensionless ratios

$$\sigma_{\text{out}}/\omega_c^2\sigma_{\text{in}}, \quad \widetilde{\sigma}_{\infty,\text{out}}/\omega_c^2\sigma_{\text{in}}, \quad \widetilde{\sigma}_{0,\text{out}}/\omega_c^2\sigma_{\text{in}},$$

are as plotted in Fig. 3.3. The maximum value of $\widetilde{\sigma}_{\infty,\text{out}}/\sigma_{\text{out}}$ is approximately 1.20. However, $\widetilde{\sigma}_{0,\text{out}}/\sigma_{\text{out}}$ is approximately $(\omega_c T/20)^{1/2}$ for large values of $\omega_c T$.

3.5 Optimum weighting functions for white noise. Design formulas. In each of the three examples of optimization worked out in the preceding sections, it was seen that the substitution of the weighting function $\widetilde{W}_\infty(\tau)$, as if $\omega_c \to \infty$, for the optimum weighting function $W(\tau)$ made very little difference in the output/input standard deviation ratio for any values of ω_c and T. Experience has shown this to be true even for noise power spectra which are considerably different from those used in these examples. In this section, therefore, we will derive formulas for the family of weighting functions which are optimum for white (i.e., flat spectrum) noise of essentially unlimited bandwidth, and we will determine the performance of these weighting functions with band-limited white noise. The formulas developed here have been found to be sufficiently accurate to serve as a basis for exploratory or feasibility studies and frequently even for the final designs.

Two methods of deriving the weighting functions will be presented (as in Blackman, Bode, and Shannon, 1948). The first method is just the one described in Section 3.1, which becomes very simple when $P(\omega) = \omega^{2r}$. The second method is based purely on weighted polynomial *curve-fitting* without explicit reference to the noise.

When $P(\omega) = \omega^{2r}$, the weighting function $W_r(\tau)$ must satisfy the differential equation

$$\frac{d^{2r}}{d\tau^{2r}} W_r(\tau) = \hat{k}(\tau),$$

where $\hat{k}(\tau)$ is some constant in the interval $0 \leq \tau \leq T$, but is otherwise determined by the requirement $W(\tau) \equiv 0$ outside of $0 \leq \tau \leq T$. Thus, in $0 \leq \tau \leq T$, $W_r(\tau)$ must be a polynomial of degree $2r$ in τ. The form of this polynomial, up to a normalizing constant factor, follows immediately from the fact that the variance $\bar{\sigma}_r^2$ of the output noise is finite only if $W_r(\tau)$ and all of its derivatives of order lower than r vanish at both $\tau = 0$ and $\tau = T$. Thus, it can only be

$$W_r(\tau) = \frac{K_r}{T}\left[\frac{\tau}{T}\left(1 - \frac{\tau}{T}\right)\right]^r \qquad \text{in } 0 \leq \tau \leq T, \qquad (3\text{–}34)$$

where, for normalization,

$$K_r = \frac{(2r + 1)!}{(r!)^2}.$$

A few of the K_r's are given in the following table.

r	K_r
0	1
1	6
2	30
3	140
4	630
5	2772

The first three of these weighting functions are the $\widetilde{W}_\infty(\tau)$ found in the three examples worked out in the preceding sections, viz., Eqs. (3–16), (3–23), and (3–30).

In the polynomial *curve-fitting* method, we are to minimize the integral

$$\int [F(\tau;t) - E(t - \tau)]^2 W_0(\tau)\, d\tau, \qquad (3\text{–}35)$$

where t, τ, and $E(t - \tau)$ have the same meanings as in Eq. (1–2); the minimization is with respect to $F(\tau;t)$, a polynomial in τ. The response time t is to be held fixed in both $F(\tau;t)$ and $E(t - \tau)$; and $W_0(\tau)$ is some weighting function which is identically zero outside of $0 \leq \tau \leq T$. It is convenient to express $F(\tau;t)$ as

$$F(\tau;t) = \sum_r V_r(t) G_r(\tau), \qquad (3\text{–}36)$$

where $G_r(\tau)$ is a polynomial of degree r in τ. Now, let

$$\int G_r(\tau) G_s(\tau) W_0(\tau)\, d\tau = \frac{1}{A_r^2} \qquad \text{if } r = s,$$

$$= 0 \qquad \text{if } r \neq s. \qquad (3\text{–}37)$$

Then, the integral (3–35) is a minimum with respect to the V's in Eq. (3–36) if

$$V_r(t) = A_r^2 \int G_r(\tau) W_0(\tau) E(t - \tau)\, d\tau.$$

Hence, $V_r(t)$ is the response of a fixed continuous scheme whose weighting function in the notation of Fig. 2.3 is

$$W_r^{(r)}(\tau) = A_r^2 G_r(\tau) W_0(\tau).\tag{3-38}$$

For a prediction time of α, the value of the polynomial (3–36) is

$$F(-\alpha;t) = \sum_r G_r(-\alpha)V_r(t),$$

whence, the multipliers in Fig. 2.3 are

$$k_r = G_r(-\alpha).\tag{3-39}$$

Equation (3–37) characterizes the $G_r(\tau)$ as orthogonal polynomials with respect to the weighting function $W_0(\tau)$. However, they are in general not normalized inasmuch as the A_r are required for the normalization of the weighting functions $W_r(\tau)$. The $G_r(\tau)$, $W_r(\tau)$, and A_r may be determined for consecutive values of r by the well-known Schmidt orthogonalization process.

The weighting functions derived by the minimization of the expression (3–35) are in general not optimum, but they are much closer to optimum (smoothing) than those defined by Eq. (3–34). In fact, they are optimum for white noise of essentially unlimited bandwidth. Thus, if

$$W_0(\tau) = \frac{1}{T} \quad \text{in } 0 \le \tau \le T,\tag{3-40}$$

then the G's are directly related to Legendre polynomials. The Legendre polynomials $P_r(x)$ are defined by Rodrigues' formula as

$$P_r(x) = \frac{1}{2^r r!} \frac{d^r}{dx^r} (x^2 - 1)^r,$$

from which it follows easily (by partial integrations) that

$$\int_{-1}^{+1} P_r(x)P_s(x)\, dx = \frac{2}{2r+1} \quad \text{if } r = s,$$

$$= 0 \quad \text{if } r \ne s.$$

Substituting $x = (2\tau/T) - 1$, we get

$$P_r\left(\frac{2\tau}{T} - 1\right) = \frac{(-T)^r}{r!} \frac{d^r}{d\tau^r}\left[\frac{\tau}{T}\left(1 - \frac{\tau}{T}\right)\right]^r,\tag{3-41}$$

and

$$\int_0^T P_r\left(\frac{2\tau}{T} - 1\right) P_s\left(\frac{2\tau}{T} - 1\right) \frac{d\tau}{T} = \frac{1}{2r+1} \quad \text{if } r = s,$$

$$= 0 \quad \text{if } r \ne s.\tag{3-42}$$

Comparing Eqs. (3–37) and (3–42), we get

$$G_r(\tau) = \frac{\sqrt{2r+1}}{A_r} P_r\left(\frac{2\tau}{T} - 1\right). \tag{3-43}$$

By Eqs. (3–38), (3–43), (3–41), and (3–40), and after an r-fold integration with respect to τ, we get

$$W_r(\tau) = A_r\sqrt{2r+1}\,\frac{(-)^r T^{r-1}}{r!}\left[\frac{\tau}{T}\left(1 - \frac{\tau}{T}\right)\right]^r$$

in $0 \leq \tau \leq T$. Now,

$$\int_0^1 [\xi(1 - \xi)]^r \, d\xi = \frac{(r!)^2}{(2r+1)!}.$$

Hence, to normalize $W_r(\tau)$ as in Eq. (3–34), we must take

$$A_r = \frac{(-)^r}{T^r}\,\frac{(2r)!\sqrt{2r+1}}{r!},$$

whence, by Eqs. (3–39) and (3–43),

$$k_r = \frac{r!}{(2r)!}\,T^r P_r\left(1 + \frac{2\alpha}{T}\right). \tag{3-44}$$

In particular,

$$k_0 = 1,$$

$$k_1 = \frac{T}{2} + \alpha,$$

$$k_2 = \frac{T^2}{12} + \frac{T\alpha}{2} + \frac{\alpha^2}{2},$$

$$k_3 = \frac{T^3}{120} + \frac{T^2\alpha}{10} + \frac{T\alpha^2}{4} + \frac{\alpha^3}{6}.$$

The transfer function $Y_r(p)$ corresponding to the weighting function $W_r(\tau)$ is

$$Y_r(p) = \frac{(2r+1)!}{r!P^{2r+1}} \sum_{s=0}^{r} \frac{(r+s)!P^{r-s}}{s!(r-s)!}[(-)^s + (-)^{r+1}e^{-P}] \qquad (P = pT).$$

In particular,

$$Y_0(p) = \frac{1}{P}(1 - e^{-P}),$$

$$Y_1(p) = \frac{6}{P^3}[(P - 2) + (P + 2)e^{-P}],$$

$$Y_2(p) = \frac{60}{P^5}[(P^2 - 6P + 12) - (P^2 + 6P + 12)e^{-P}].$$

With $p = i\omega$, these may be expressed in the form

$$Y_r(i\omega) = Q_r(\phi)e^{-i\phi} \qquad \left(\phi = \frac{\omega T}{2}\right),$$

where

$$Q_0(\phi) = \frac{\sin \phi}{\phi},$$

$$Q_1(\phi) = \frac{3}{\phi^3}(\sin \phi - \phi \cos \phi),$$

$$Q_2(\phi) = \frac{15}{\phi^5}[(3 - \phi^2) \sin \phi - 3\phi \cos \phi].$$

If the noise is band-limited white noise with a spectral density of $\sigma^2/2f_c$ per cycle/sec in the interval $-f_c < f < f_c$, the ratio of the output noise variance $\bar{\sigma}_r^2$ in the notation of Fig. 2.2 to the input noise variance σ^2 is given by

$$\frac{\bar{\sigma}_r^2}{\sigma^2} = \frac{1}{\omega_c} \int_0^{\omega_c} \omega^{2r} |Y_r(i\omega)|^2 \, d\omega \qquad (\omega_c = 2\pi f_c)$$

$$= \frac{\omega_c^{2r}}{2r + 1} F_r(a) \qquad (a = \omega_c T), \qquad (3\text{-}45)$$

where, for example,

$$F_0(a) = \frac{2}{a}\left[\text{Si }(a) - \frac{1 - \cos a}{a}\right],$$

$$F_1(a) = \frac{72}{a^3}\left\{\text{Si }(a) - \frac{1}{a^3}[4 + 3a^2 - (4 + a^2)\cos a - 4a \sin a]\right\}.$$

The factor $\omega_c^{2r}/(2r + 1)$ in Eq. (3-45) is obviously the value of the variance ratio $\bar{\sigma}_r^2/\sigma^2$ in the absence of smoothing (that is, with $|Y_r(i\omega)| = 1$). Hence, $F_r(a)$ is the factor by which the variance ratio is reduced by smoothing. Figure 3.4 is a plot of $F_1(a)$. It is typical of the plots of all of the $F_r(a)$ for which the asymptotes are

$$F_r(a) \to 1 \qquad \text{as } a \to 0,$$

and

$$F_r(a) \to \frac{2r + 1}{\omega_c^{2r+1}} \int_0^\infty \omega^{2r} |Y_r(i\omega)|^2 \, d\omega,$$

$$\to \frac{(2r + 1)\pi}{\omega_c^{2r+1}} \int [W_r^{(r)}(\tau)]^2 \, d\tau,$$

$$\to \left[\frac{(2r + 1)!}{r!}\right]^2 \frac{\pi}{a^{2r+1}} \qquad \text{as } a \to \infty.$$

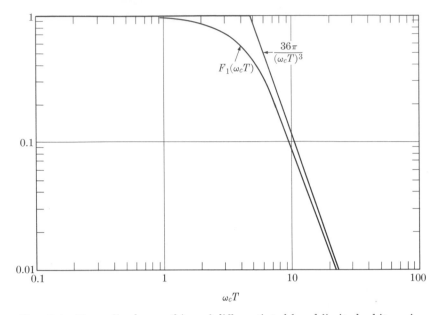

$$F_1(\omega_c T) \qquad \frac{36\pi}{(\omega_c T)^3}$$

$$\omega_c T$$

FIG. 3.4. Normalized smoothing of differentiated band-limited white noise.

(The last step is most easily made through the Legendre polynomials.) Since the object of smoothing in practice is to achieve the condition

$$\frac{\bar{\sigma}_r^2}{\sigma^2} \ll \frac{\omega_c^{2r}}{2r+1}, \tag{3-46}$$

the approximation

$$\frac{\bar{\sigma}_r^2}{\sigma^2} \approx \frac{(2r)!(2r+1)!}{2(r!)^2 f_c T^{2r+1}}, \tag{3-47}$$

which should be very close if $T \gg 1/f_c$, may be used, at least for exploratory or feasibility studies. A few of the numerical coefficients involved in this formula are given in the following table.

r	$(2r)!(2r+1)!/2(r!)^2$
0	$\frac{1}{2}$
1	6
2	360
3	50400
4	12,700,800
5	5,029,516,800

For purposes of the approximate realizations described in the next chapter, we need the power series expansions of the transfer functions $Y_r(p)$ corresponding to the weighting functions $W_r(\tau)$. In general, we have

$$Y_r(p) = \frac{(2r+1)!}{r!} \sum_{m=0}^{\infty} \frac{(m+r)!(-pT)^m}{m!(m+2r+1)!}. \tag{3-48}$$

In particular, we have

$$Y_0(p) = 1 - \tfrac{1}{2}P + \tfrac{1}{6}P^2 - \tfrac{1}{24}P^3 + \tfrac{1}{120}P^4 - \tfrac{1}{720}P^5 + \tfrac{1}{5040}P^6 - \cdots,$$

$$Y_1(p) = 1 - \tfrac{1}{2}P + \tfrac{3}{20}P^2 - \tfrac{1}{30}P^3 + \tfrac{1}{168}P^4 - \tfrac{1}{1120}P^5 + \cdots,$$

$$Y_2(p) = 1 - \tfrac{1}{2}P + \tfrac{1}{7}P^2 - \tfrac{5}{168}P^3 + \tfrac{5}{1008}P^4 - \cdots,$$

$$Y_3(p) = 1 - \tfrac{1}{2}P + \tfrac{5}{36}P^2 - \tfrac{1}{36}P^3 + \cdots,$$

$$Y_4(p) = 1 - \tfrac{1}{2}P + \tfrac{3}{22}P^2 - \cdots,$$

$$Y_5(p) = 1 - \tfrac{1}{2}P + \cdots,$$

where $P = pT$.

3.6 Determination of polynomial degree and smoothing time. So far, we have not considered the determination of the best values of the degree n of polynomial approximation, and the smoothing time T. Unfortunately, there is no practically useful theory of complete optimization including the determination of n and T. What we have done in the preceding chapter and up to this point in the present chapter is to lay a foundation for a numerical cut-and-try method of determining the best values of n and T. This method is rigorous in principle, but in order to make it simpler for practical use we have worked out some approximations in the basic formulas. Experience has shown that the effects of these approximations are usually negligible in view of uncertainties over which we have no control.

In the preceding chapter we considered the effect of smoothing and prediction on the signal component of the data, and we developed a formula for estimating the *systematic* (or *dynamic*) error. This error depends upon n, T, and the shapes of the weighting functions $W_r(\tau)$. The determination of the shapes of the weighting functions was deferred to this chapter, but it was possible in the preceding chapter to show that if these shapes are optimum in a well-defined sense, the noise outputs of the smoothers are uncorrelated.

In the present chapter we considered the effects of smoothing on the noise component in successive derivatives of the data. Although the optimum shapes of the weighting functions depend upon T and the shape of the noise spectrum in a complicated way, the output/input variance ratios are reasonably insensitive to departures in a certain direction from the optimum shapes. This allowed us to standardize the shapes of the weighting functions. On this basis, we then went on to develop *design formulas* under the assumption of wideband bandlimited white noise.

One way of determining the "best" values of n and T is simply to compute the *systematic* and *random* errors for a sufficient number of pairs of values of

n and T to plot curves of the form shown in Fig. 3.5. The necessary formulas for continuous schemes are (2–13) of the preceding chapter, and (3–44) and (3–47) of the present chapter. The cross-correlation between the noise outputs of the smoothers may be neglected.

This method of determining n and T (which was used in connection with the design of a fixed discrete scheme) is different from the one described in Blackman, Bode, and Shannon, 1948. In the latter (chronologically earlier) case, as noted in the introductory remarks in Chapter 2, the signal component of the data was assumed to be piecewise polynomial with Poisson distribution of discontinuities in time. This assumption was based on a substantial amount of recorded data relevant to the specific problem, which supported the view that a particular value of n would be satisfactory most of the time and that the next higher value of n would provide a slight improvement some of the time. The choice of T was to have been based on the distribution of discontinuities (more exactly, the distribution of intervals between discontinuities), but this was superseded by other considerations.

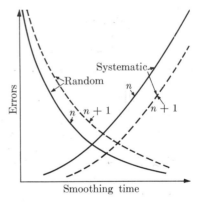

Fig. 3.5. Determination of degree of polynomial and smoothing time.

The difference between the two methods of determining n and T is an example of the fact noted in the opening remark in Chapter 2, that the development of a theory of prediction with optimum smoothing depends to a large extent upon the initial knowledge and/or assumptions with respect to the characteristics of the signal component and the noise component of the data. In the Kolmogorov and Wiener theories, the question of determining n and T does not arise at all because the signal component, as well as the noise component, is assumed to have no structure whatsoever, apart from correlated randomness (see Bode and Shannon, 1950).

In the next three sections, and in the last section of Chapter 8, we will consider some situations in which the determination of n is largely irrelevant for other reasons.

3.7 An application of the minimax criterion of game theory. Consider a hostile airplane and a missile initially on a straight head-on collision course. The airplane then attempts by maneuvering to avoid interception, and the missile is to be steered in an attempt to ensure interception. Assuming that the airplane happens to execute the best maneuver for maximum miss distance, we want to know how the missile should be steered in order to minimize the maximum miss distance.

Let $X(t)$ and $\hat{X}(t)$ be the displacements of the airplane and missile, respectively, from the line of the original head-on collision course. In the absence of noise, let

$$\hat{X}(t) = \int X(t - \tau)W(\tau)\, d\tau,$$

where according to our convention the range of integration is formally from $-\infty$ to $+\infty$, although physical realizability demands that

$$W(\tau) = 0 \qquad \text{for all } \tau < 0. \tag{3–49}$$

The systematic error is, therefore,

$$E_s(t) = \hat{X}(t) - X(t) = \int X(t - \tau)[W(\tau) - \delta(\tau)]\, d\tau. \tag{3–50}$$

The weighting function $W(\tau)$ should at least be of such a form that the systematic error will be zero if the airplane did not maneuver for a time interval of at least T. Substituting $X(t) = a + bt$, we get

$$E_s(t) = (a + bt)\left[\int W(\tau)\, d\tau - 1\right] - b \int \tau W(\tau)\, d\tau.$$

Hence, in addition to (3–49), we will require

$$W(\tau) = 0 \qquad \text{for all } \tau > T, \tag{3–51}$$

$$\int W(\tau)\, d\tau = 1, \tag{3–52}$$

$$\int \tau W(\tau)\, d\tau = 0. \tag{3–53}$$

The next step is to express the systematic error in terms of the acceleration of the airplane away from the line of the original head-on collision course. To this end, let

$$V(\tau) = g(\tau) - \tau \int_{-\infty}^{\tau} W(\xi)\, d\xi + \int_{-\infty}^{\tau} \xi W(\xi)\, d\xi, \tag{3–54}$$

where

$$g(\tau) = 0 \qquad \text{for all } \tau < 0,$$
$$\qquad = \tau \qquad \text{for all } \tau > 0. \tag{3–55}$$

Note that $V(\tau) = 0$ for all $\tau < 0$ on account of (3–49) and (3–55), and that $V(\tau) = 0$ also for all $\tau > T$ on account of (3–51), (3–52), (3–53), and (3–55).

Differentiating (3–54), we get

$$V^{(1)}(\tau) = h(\tau) - \int_{-\infty}^{\tau} W(\xi) \, d\xi,$$

where

$$
\begin{aligned}
h(\tau) &= 0 \qquad \text{for all } \tau < 0, \\
&= 1 \qquad \text{for all } \tau > 0.
\end{aligned}
\tag{3–56}
$$

Note that $V^{(1)}(\tau) = 0$ for all $\tau < 0$ on account of (3–49) and (3–56) and that $V^{(1)}(\tau) = 0$ also for all $\tau > T$ on account of (3–51), (3–52), and (3–56). Differentiating once more, we get

$$V^{(2)}(\tau) = \delta(\tau) - W(\tau).
\tag{3–57}$$

Substituting this into (3–50), and performing two partial integrations, remembering that $V^{(1)}(\pm\infty) = 0$ and $V(\pm\infty) = 0$, we get

$$E_s(t) = - \int \ddot{X}(t - \tau) V(\tau) \, d\tau.$$

If the airplane has a maximum acceleration capability of A and is capable of reversing its acceleration instantaneously, then

$$\max |E_s| = A \int |V(\tau)| \, d\tau.
\tag{3–58}$$

Now, let us consider the effect of noise. The variance of the random component of miss distance due to noise is

$$\text{var} \{E_r\} = \int P(f) |Y(i\omega)|^2 \, df \qquad (\omega = 2\pi f),$$

where $P(f)$ is the two-sided power spectrum of the observational errors, and $Y(i\omega)$ is the transfer function corresponding to the weighting function $W(\tau)$. For definiteness, we will assume

$$
\begin{aligned}
P(f) &= \frac{\sigma^2}{2f_c} \qquad \text{for all } |f| < f_c \\
&= 0 \qquad \text{for all } |f| > f_c.
\end{aligned}
$$

Then,

$$\text{var} \{E_r\} = \frac{\sigma^2}{2f_c} \int_{-f_c}^{f_c} |Y(i\omega)|^2 \, df.$$

We will also assume that the power transfer function $|Y(i\omega)|^2$ is so small for all $|f| > f_c$ that we may write, to a very good approximation,

$$\text{var} \{E_r\} = \frac{\sigma^2}{2f_c} \int |Y(i\omega)|^2 \, df,$$

and, therefore, by Parseval's theorem,

$$\text{var } \{E_r\} = \frac{\sigma^2}{2f_c} \int [W(\tau)]^2 \, d\tau. \tag{3-59}$$

Next, let us consider the following specific cases.

Case	$W(\tau), \, 0 < \tau < T$	$V(\tau), \, 0 < \tau < T$	$\int \tau^2 W(\tau) \, d\tau$
1	$\dfrac{2}{T}\left(2 - \dfrac{3\tau}{T}\right)$	$\tau\left(1 - \dfrac{\tau}{T}\right)^2$	$-\dfrac{T^2}{6}$
2	$\dfrac{3}{T}\left(3 - \dfrac{12\tau}{T} + \dfrac{10\tau^2}{T^2}\right)$	$\tau\left(1 - \dfrac{5\tau}{2T}\right)\left(1 - \dfrac{\tau}{T}\right)^2$	0
3	$\dfrac{6}{T}\left(1 - \dfrac{2\tau}{T}\right)\left(1 - \dfrac{\tau}{T}\right)$	$\tau\left(1 - \dfrac{\tau}{T}\right)^3$	$-\dfrac{T^2}{10}$
4	$\dfrac{8}{T}\left(1 - \dfrac{5\tau}{2T}\right)\left(1 - \dfrac{\tau}{T}\right)^2$	$\tau\left(1 - \dfrac{\tau}{T}\right)^4$	$-\dfrac{T^2}{15}$

The $W(\tau)$ in Case 1 is the simplest doubly truncated polynomial satisfying (3–52) and (3–53). The $W(\tau)$ in Case 2 is the simplest with zero second moment. The $V(\tau)$ in Cases 1, 3, and 4 form a sequence with no sign reversal. The $V(\tau)$ in Case 2 reverses sign at $\tau = 2T/5$. By Eqs. (3–58) and (3–59), we get the following results.

Case	$\dfrac{1}{AT^2} \max |E_s|$	$\dfrac{2f_cT}{\sigma^2} \text{var } \{E_r\}$
1	$\frac{1}{12}$	4
2	$\frac{108}{3125}$	9
3	$\frac{1}{20}$	$\frac{24}{5}$
4	$\frac{1}{30}$	$\frac{208}{35}$

In each case, we have

$$\max |E_s| = aAT^2,$$

$$\text{var } \{E_r\} = \frac{b\sigma^2}{2f_cT},$$

where a and b are the tabulated numbers. If E is defined by

$$\text{ave } \{E^2\} = \max |E_s|^2 + \text{var } \{E_r\}, \tag{3-60}$$

then ave $\{E^2\}$ is a minimum with respect to T when

$$\left(\frac{f_cA^2}{\sigma^2}\right)^{1/5} T = \left(\frac{b}{8a^2}\right)^{1/5}. \tag{3-61}$$

Hence, we have

$$\left(\frac{f_c}{\sigma^2\sqrt{A}}\right)^{4/5} \text{min ave } \{E^2\} = 5\left(\frac{b\sqrt{a}}{8}\right)^{4/5}. \tag{3-62}$$

Thus

Case	(3–61)	(3–62)
1	2.352	1.063
2	3.934	1.430
3	2.993	1.002
4	3.673	1.011

Note that Case 2, with the zero second moment of $W(\tau)$, is the least favorable to interception. Case 3 is the most favorable. However, the rms miss for the former is only about 20% greater than for the latter. From a practical point of view, this difference would usually be regarded as not important.

Since

$$\text{ave } \{E^2\} = \left[A\int |V(\tau)|\, d\tau\right]^2 + \frac{\sigma^2}{2f_c}\int [W(\tau)]^2\, d\tau,$$

where $V(\tau)$ and $W(\tau)$ are related by (3–57), it follows, by the variational calculus, that ave $\{E^2\}$ is stationary with respect to variations of $V(\tau)$ or $W(\tau)$ in $0 < \tau < T$ if

$$W^{(2)}(\tau) = \pm\frac{2f_cA^2}{\sigma^2}\int |V(\tau)|\, d\tau, \tag{3-63}$$

where the upper sign must hold at values of τ for which $V(\tau) > 0$, and the lower sign must hold at values of τ for which $V(\tau) < 0$. Since the right-hand side, except for sign, is a constant, $W^{(2)}(\tau)$ must be piecewise constant, with the same absolute value throughout $0 \le \tau \le T$, but with changes of sign at values of τ where $V(\tau)$ changes sign. This necessary condition is not fulfilled in Cases 1, 2, and 4. Substituting the expressions for $W(\tau)$ and $V(\tau)$ for Case 3, we get

$$\frac{24}{T^3} = \frac{2f_cA^2T^2}{\sigma^2}\int_0^1 \xi(1 - \xi)^3\, d\xi$$

$$= \frac{f_cA^2T^2}{10\sigma^2},$$

whence

$$\frac{f_cA^2T^5}{\sigma^2} = 240.$$

This agrees with (3–61), since $a = \frac{1}{20}$ and $b = \frac{24}{5}$. Hence, Case 3 is optimum.

In the optimum case,

$$\text{max }|E_s| = \frac{1}{20}AT^2 = \left(\frac{3\sigma^2}{5f_cT}\right)^{1/2},$$

$$\text{var }\{E_r\} = \frac{12}{5}\frac{\sigma^2}{f_cT} = \frac{1}{100}(AT^2)^2.$$

Thus, we have

$$\frac{\operatorname{var}\{E_r\}}{\max|E_s|^2} = 4,$$

and

$$\operatorname{ave}\{E^2\} = \frac{1}{80}(AT^2)^2.$$

The value of max $|E_s|$ arises in the following way. While the airplane is accelerating at its maximum value of A during the time interval T, the missile, in the absence of noise, would be accelerating at

$$\frac{A\tau}{T}\left(6 - \frac{9\tau}{T} + \frac{4\tau^2}{T^2}\right) \qquad (0 \le \tau \le T),$$

where τ is time after the airplane started its acceleration. Thus, at the end of the time interval T, the target and the missile would have undergone transverse displacements of $AT^2/2$ and $9AT^2/20$, respectively. The missile acceleration would reach a maximum value of $5A/4$, halfway through the time interval T, after which it would decrease to A at the end of the interval. Then both the airplane and the missile would have the same transverse velocity, AT, so that, if both continued to accelerate at the value A, the difference between their transverse displacements would remain constant at $AT^2/20$.

With the airplane maneuver assumed in the preceding paragraph and with $W(\tau)$ of Case 2, the missile acceleration (in the absence of noise) would be

$$\frac{A\tau}{T}\left(9 - \frac{18\tau}{T} + \frac{10\tau^2}{T^2}\right) \qquad (0 \le \tau \le T).$$

Thus, at the end of the interval T, the acceleration, velocity, and displacement of the missile would be A, AT, and $AT^2/2$, respectively. However, var $\{E_r\} = (3/160)(AT^2)^2$, which is larger than the ave $\{E^2\}$ for the optimum case. Furthermore, if the airplane were to reverse its acceleration after an interval of $2T/5$, the error $|E_s|$ at the end of the interval T would be $108AT^2/3125$. Thus,

$$\operatorname{ave}\{E^2\} \approx \frac{1}{50}(AT^2)^2.$$

3.8 Guided rockets. Consider a rocket whose motion is assumed for simplicity to be confined to a fixed plane. The direction of its motion is subject to the force of gravity, to atmospheric drag, and to meteorological perturbations but is otherwise controlled (although its response is not instantaneous) by steering commands sent to it from the ground through a radio communications link. Its position is monitored by a radar tracker which perforce introduces tracking errors. The guidance loop is closed through the data-processing scheme outlined in Fig. 3.6 in which the blank box is first assumed to be made up as shown in Fig. 3.7. Now, let us assume that (a) the smoothing time can be made short enough to make the system stable, and the systematic errors tolerable, but then the random errors are intolerable; (b) it is impossible to increase the smoothing time without either making the system unstable, or making the systematic errors intolerable, before the random errors become tolerable; and (c) delay correction, which in effect involves increasing the degree n of polynomial approximation, makes the situation worse or at least no better. Clearly, we must look for another modification of the data-processing scheme.

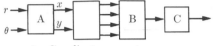

A   Coordinate converter
B   Steering error computer
C   Steering command computer

FIG. 3.6.   Block diagram of a guidance computer.

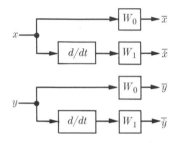

FIG. 3.7.   Tentative details of blank box in Fig. 3.6.

Such a modification of the data-processing scheme is possible if the response characteristics of the rocket and the tracker are known at least approximately. These characteristics are designed into the simulator in Fig. 3.8 which generates approximations to the signal constituents of x, $\dot{x}$, y, and $\dot{y}$. These approximations are subtracted from the inputs to the smoothers and are added back to the outputs of the smoothers. Thus the feedback from the output to the input of the steering command computer is dependent to a much smaller extent upon the smoothing time. The smoothing time may now be increased more than in the previous arrangement without either making the system unstable or making the systematic errors intolerable.

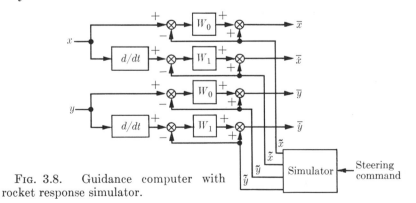

FIG. 3.8.   Guidance computer with rocket response simulator.

Unfortunately, the response characteristic of the rocket is usually such that the system would be unstable even if the smoothing time were reduced to zero in the original arrangement of the data-processing scheme. Then, of course, the system would be just as unstable with the modification described above. To get around this difficulty another modification was suggested by S. Darlington in 1947. The essence of Darlington's suggestion is shown in Fig. 3.9, where $Y_1(p)/p$ is the transfer function from the output of the steering command computer to the adder at the input of the steering command computer through the actual rocket and $Y_2(p)/p$ is what that transfer function would be if the rocket had a faster response characteristic. In principle, we may take $Y_2(p) = Y_1(0)$, but this extreme choice has some practical drawbacks. However, it is convenient and advantageous to take $Y_2(0) = Y_1(0)$ so that $(Y_2 - Y_1)/p$ will not have a pole at $p = 0$. A simple approximation to $(Y_2 - Y_1)/p$ may be derived by the method of moments described in the next chapter. Some adjustment of the approximation by methods which are familiar to feedback amplifier designers (Bode, 1945) may be required in order to secure adequate margins of stability for the entire dynamical system.

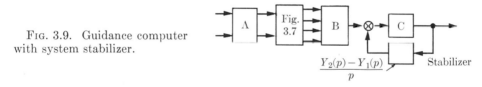

FIG. 3.9. Guidance computer with system stabilizer.

Two other guidance schemes are described in some detail in Myers and Thompson (1961) and in Evans, Myers, and Timko (1963).

3.9 Multi-instrument schemes. The earliest disclosure of the advantages of using data gathered by two or more different kinds of observational instruments is probably that of Crooks (1948). This idea has been proposed or described in various connections by Darlington (1950, 1954), Stewart and Parks (1957), Bendat (1957a, 1958), Darlington (1958), and Ling (1958). The idea is illustrated by the following simple one-dimensional example.

Let $x_1(t)$ be the observed position obtained by a tracker and $\ddot{x}_2(t)$ be the observed acceleration obtained by an accelerometer. Consider the output of a data-processing scheme, expressed by the operational equation

$$V(t) = pY_1(p)x_1(t) + Y_2(p)\ddot{x}_2(t).$$

In the absence of noise, $x_1(t)$ is the true position $x(t)$, and $\ddot{x}_2(t)$ is the true acceleration $\ddot{x}(t)$. Then, $V(t)$ is the true velocity $\dot{x}(t)$, provided that

$$Y_1(p) + pY_2(p) = 1.$$

Hence

$$Y_2(p) = \frac{1 - Y_1(p)}{p}.\qquad\qquad (3\text{–}64)$$

Note that if $V(t)$ is to be the true velocity in the absence of acceleration and noise, we must have $Y_1(0) = 1$. Hence, $Y_2(p)$ will have no pole at $p = 0$.

We now assume that the accelerometer error is constant with time but that it is quantitatively a random variable having a probability distribution with average zero and variance σ_2^2. (This type of error is an example of a stationary random process which is not ergodic because its statistical properties are not the same over time as over the ensemble.) On the other hand, we assume that the tracking noise is ergodic and band-limited white with average zero, variance σ_1^2, and cut-off frequency f_c.

If the weighting functions $W_1(\tau)$ and $W_2(\tau)$ corresponding to the transfer functions $Y_1(p)$ and $Y_2(p)$ are constrained to be zero outside of the interval $0 \leq \tau \leq T$, where $T \gg 1/f_c$, then the output noise variance is (very nearly)

$$\sigma_V^2 = \frac{\sigma_1^2}{2f_c} \int_0^T \left[\frac{d}{d\tau} W_1(\tau) \right]^2 d\tau + \sigma_2^2 \left[\int_0^T W_2(\tau) \, d\tau \right]^2,$$

where, by Eq. (3–64),

$$W_2(\tau) = 1 - \int_0^\tau W_1(\xi) \, d\xi, \qquad 0 \leq \tau \leq T.$$

By the calculus of variations, it is easily determined that, in order to minimize σ_V^2, $W_1(\tau)$ must be a polynomial of third degree in τ; and since it must have unit area and must vanish at $\tau = 0$ and $\tau = T$, we may take it in the form

$$W_1(\tau) = \frac{6\tau}{T^2} \left(1 - \frac{\tau}{T} \right) \left[1 + A \left(1 - \frac{2\tau}{T} \right) \right], \qquad 0 \leq \tau \leq T,$$

with

$$W_2(\tau) = \left(1 - \frac{\tau}{T} \right)^2 \left(1 + \frac{2\tau}{T} - \frac{3A\tau^2}{T^2} \right), \qquad 0 \leq \tau \leq T,$$

where A is to be determined. Thus

$$\sigma_V^2 = \frac{6\sigma_1^2}{5f_c T^3} (5 + 3A^2) + \frac{T^2 \sigma_2^2}{100} (5 - A)^2$$

is minimum when

$$A = \frac{5f_c T^5 \sigma_2^2}{360\sigma_1^2 + f_c T^5 \sigma_2^2},$$

and then

$$[\sigma_V^2]_{min} = \frac{48\sigma_1^2}{f_c T^3} \frac{45\sigma_1^2 + 2f_c T^5 \sigma_2^2}{360\sigma_1^2 + f_c T^5 \sigma_2^2}.$$

Then also,

$$W_1(\tau) = \frac{6}{T} \left[\frac{\tau}{T} \left(1 - \frac{\tau}{T} \right) \right] + k \frac{d}{d\tau} \left\{ 30 \left[\frac{\tau}{T} \left(1 - \frac{\tau}{T} \right) \right]^2 \right\},$$

where $k = AT/10$. In this formula for $W_1(\tau)$, we can recognize two of the weighting functions specified by Eq. (3–34) and the combination as a special case of Fig. 2.2 in the preceding chapter.

Alternatively, we may simplify both weighting functions by taking $A = 0$, arbitrarily and minimizing σ_V^2 with respect to T by taking

$$T^5 = \frac{36\sigma_1^2}{f_c\sigma_2^2}.$$

Then,

$$[\sigma_V^2]_{min} = 15 \left(\frac{\sigma_1^2}{f_c}\right)^{2/5} \left(\frac{\sigma_2^2}{36}\right)^{3/5}.$$

Aside from the use of an accelerometer to measure the actual acceleration of the vehicle in this example, the functional similarity of Eq. (3–64) to that of the stabilizer in Fig. 3.9 should be noted.

CHAPTER 4

PRACTICAL ANALOG APPROXIMATIONS

In this chapter we will review briefly a few of the practical analog approximations which have been worked out for the weighting functions described by Eqs. (3–34). In particular, we will consider approximations to $W_0(\tau)$, $W_1(\tau)$, $W_2(\tau)$, and $W_{1,3}(\tau)$ where

$$W_{1,3}(\tau) = W_1(\tau) + \frac{T}{2} W_2'(\tau) + \frac{T^2}{10} W_3''(\tau).$$

4.1 Method of moments. These approximations (rational functions of $p = i\omega$) were all obtained by the *method of moments* (Perron, 1913; Blackman-Bode-Shannon, 1948; Ba Hli, 1954) which makes implicit use of the relations established in Chapter 2 between the moments of a weighting function and the coefficients in the power series expansion of the transfer function. According to the method of moments, if we wish to approximate the weighting function $W(\tau)$, which we may assume to have unit area (zeroth moment), out to the $(m + n)$th moment, we should take the formula

$$\tilde{Y}(p) = \frac{1 + a_1 p + \cdots + a_m p^m}{1 + b_1 p + \cdots + b_n p^n}$$

and determine the coefficients so that the power series expansion of $\tilde{Y}(p)$ will be the same as the power series expansion of $Y(p) = \mathfrak{F}[W(\tau)]$, up to the term of $(m + n)$th degree. As far as the approximations to any single one of $W_r(\tau)$ are concerned, we must take $n - m > r$, because the power spectral density of r-fold differentiated white noise increases like ω^{2r}. We have always taken $n - m = r + 1$, although in one case, as we will see later, the last coefficient in the numerator turned out to be zero, so that we might just as well have taken $n - m = r + 2$.

The determination of the coefficients in $\tilde{Y}(p)$ involves the solution of a set of $(m + n)$ linear equations, of which the last n do not involve any of the coefficients in the numerator of $\tilde{Y}(p)$. These equations are obtained by equating coefficients of corresponding powers of p in the two members of the single "equation"

$$1 + a_1 p + \cdots + a_m p^m$$
$$= (1 + b_1 p + \cdots + b_n p^n)(1 + c_1 p + \cdots + c_{m+n} p^{m+n} + \cdots),$$

in which the second factor in the right-hand member is the power series expansion of the transfer function $Y(p)$ to be approximated.

These approximate transfer functions have generally been realized with a circuit of the form shown in Fig. 4.1 (U.S. Patent 2,549,065, R. L. Dietzold, April 17, 1951) or with several such circuits in tandem. The amplifier in this circuit has about 85 db gain (voltage ratio μ of about 1.8×10^4) from zero to several hundred cycles/sec, thereafter cutting off at an average rate of 9 db per octave (30 db per decade) until the loop gain is well below 0 db. The networks are resistance-capacity networks, and the feedback network is generally designed to provide a pure capacitive path from amplifier output to amplifier input so that stability is controlled mainly by the amplifier gain characteristic.

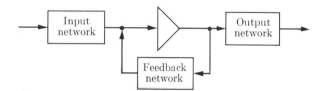

FIG. 4.1.   General method of realizing transfer functions with RC networks.

The transfer function is usually resolved into a product of simple transfer functions, sometimes with redundant frequency-dependent factors which are introduced into the numerator of one component transfer function and into the denominator of another component transfer function. Each component transfer function is realized either with a forward network (input, interamplifier, or output) or with a feedback network (see Fig. 4.1). A component transfer function with complex poles cannot be realized as a forward network, but if it has only real roots and if the denominator is just one degree higher than the numerator, then its reciprocal may be realized as the transfer function of a feedback network.

Each component transfer function is regarded as (complex) micromhos between a zero-impedance voltage source and a zero-impedance current load. (Because of parallel feedback and high loop-gain, the input and output impedances of the amplifier are virtually zero.) The load current is regarded to be in microamperes so that resistances come out directly in megohms and capacitances come out directly in microfarads.

A few of the most commonly used network configurations are given in Appendix B, before they are modified to include temperature compensation. Temperature-compensated network configurations were designed by I. E. Wood.

4.2 Approximations to $Y_0(p)$.   The noise associated with data before any differentiations are performed is usually so small that, with only one exception, the approximation $\widetilde{Y}_0(p) = 1$ has generally been used. In the one exceptional case, the main purpose of a more elaborate approximation was delay rather than smoothing. (The three branches in Fig. 2.3 were required to have the same delay.)

The next simplest approximation,

$$\tilde{Y}_0(p) = \frac{1}{1 + (T/2)p},$$

was rejected because the corresponding step response takes $2.65T$ seconds to settle to within $\frac{1}{2}\%$ of unity. The next approximation,

$$\tilde{Y}_0(p) = \frac{1 + a_1 p}{1 + b_1 p + b_2 p^2},$$

is the case mentioned earlier in which it turns out that $a_1 = 0$. In fact,

$$\tilde{Y}_0(p) = \frac{1}{1 + (T/2)p + (T^2/12)p^2}$$

$$= 1 - \tfrac{1}{2}P + \tfrac{1}{6}P^2 - \tfrac{1}{24}P^3 + \tfrac{1}{144}P^4 - \cdots,$$

where $P = pT$. (See the formulas at the end of Section 3.5.) The impulse response (weighting function) is shown in Fig. 4.2: the step response (settling characteristic) in Fig. 4.3. The step response overshoots by less than $\frac{1}{2}\%$, and it takes only $1.41T$ seconds to settle to within $\frac{1}{2}\%$ of unity.

Although smoothing was not the object here, it is of some interest to see how this approximation compares with the original. Using the formula for I_2 in Appendix C, we get

$$\frac{\sigma^2}{\omega_c} \int_0^\infty |\tilde{Y}_0(i\omega)|^2 \, d\omega = \frac{\sigma^2}{2f_c T}.$$

This is (fortuitously) exactly the same as for the original weighting function

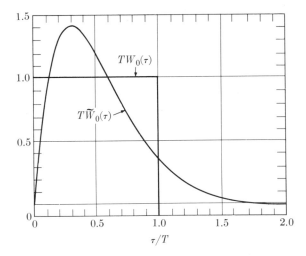

FIG. 4.2. Approximation to impulse response or weighting function $TW_0(\tau)$.

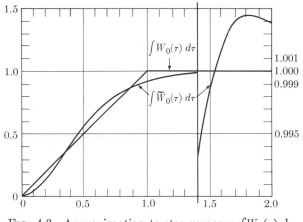

FIG. 4.3. Approximation to step response $\int W_0(\tau)\,d\tau$.

$W_0(\tau)$ with the same value of T. However, an appreciable part of the smoothing is due to the tail of the weighting function ($\tau > T$ in Fig. 4.2).

For physical realization, a redundant frequency-dependent factor was introduced, so that

$$\widetilde{Y}_0(p) = \frac{1}{1 + (T/6)p} \frac{1 + (T/6)p}{1 + (T/2)p + (T^2/12)p^2}.$$

The first component was realized as an input network (Fig. B.1, in Appendix B) and the reciprocal of the second component as a feedback network (Fig. B.6, with no resistance in the shunt branch of the bridged-T configuration).

4.3 Approximations to $Y_1(p)$. The simplest and most often used approximation to $Y_1(p)$ is

$$\widetilde{Y}_1(p) - \frac{1}{1 + (T/2)p + (T^2/10)p^2}$$

$$= 1 - \tfrac{1}{2}P + \tfrac{3}{20}P^2 - \tfrac{1}{40}P^3 + \cdots,$$

where $P = pT$. The impulse response (weighting function) is shown in Fig. 4.4, the step response (settling characteristic) in Fig. 4.5. The step response settles to within 1.75% of unity in $1.18T$ sec.

Using the formula for I_2 in Appendix C, we get

$$\frac{\sigma^2}{\omega_c} \int_0^\infty \omega^2 |\widetilde{Y}_1(i\omega)|^2 \, d\omega = \frac{5\sigma^2}{f_c T^3}.$$

This is actually smaller (by a factor of $\tfrac{5}{6}$) than for the original weighting function $W_1(\tau)$ with the same value of T. This apparently better-than-optimum result is due to the tail of $\widetilde{W}_1(\tau)$ beyond $\tau = T$.

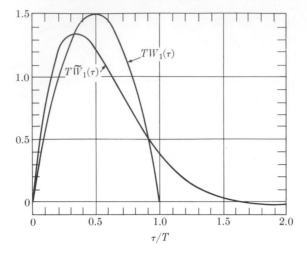

FIG. 4.4. Approximation to impulse response or weighting function $TW_1(\tau)$.

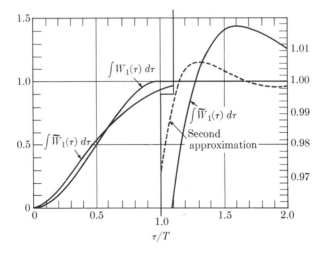

FIG. 4.5. Approximations to step response $\int W_1(\tau)\,d\tau$.

For physical realization, a redundant frequency-dependent factor was introduced, so that

$$p\tilde{Y}_1(p) = \frac{p}{1 + (T/5)p} \cdot \frac{1 + (T/5)p}{1 + (T/2)p + (T^2/10)p^2}.$$

The first component was realized as an input network (Fig. B.2), and the reciprocal of the second component as a feedback network (Fig. B.6, with no resistance in the shunt branch of the bridged-T configuration).

4.4 Preloading and protecting against overload. For further discussion, consider the physical realization of $p\widetilde{Y}_1(p)$ as shown in Fig. 4.6. At the instant that data is first applied to the circuit, there will be, effectively, a velocity impulse equal in magnitude to the initial value of the data. For example, if the initial value of the data is 100,000 ft, there will be, effectively, a velocity impulse of 100,000 ft/sec. Then, if $T = 5$, Fig. 4.4 shows that there will be a transient response which reaches a value of

$$\frac{1.35}{5} 10^5 = 27,000 \text{ ft/sec,}$$

about 1.70 sec after the data are applied. If the circuit is scaled for a maximum of 1500 ft/sec, it will be overloaded by a factor of 18. It may take the circuit more time to recover from the overload than is tolerable. This may be avoided by the switch circuitry shown in Fig. 4.6. The switch is kept closed when no data are being received and opened only after data have begun to come in. The resistance R should be as small as possible, consistent with the requirement that the preceding amplifier must also be protected from current overload. However, the output will still settle in accordance with Fig. 4.5.

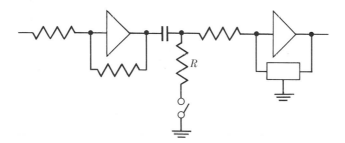

F_{IG}. 4.6. Smoothed first-derivative circuit with protection against overload and with provision for preloading.

It should be noted that the settling time of the circuit after the switch is opened may be substantially shortened if an estimate of the initial velocity is available (as for a missile at the end of vertical boost, before guidance). Such an estimate may be incorporated as a D-C voltage in series with R and the switch in Fig. 4.6. If the estimate were in error by as much as 10% the step response would settle to within 0.18% in $1.81T$ sec.

4.5 Better approximations to $Y_1(p)$. In one application, the necessity for the introduction of a redundant frequency-dependent factor was avoided and the settling characteristic was improved by using the approximation

$$\widetilde{Y}_1(p) = \frac{1 + (T/70)p}{1 + (18T/35)p + (3T^2/28)p^2 + (41T^3/4200)p^3}.$$

The step response (settling characteristic) is shown by the broken curve in Fig. 4.5. It settles to within 0.62% of unity in $1.10T$ sec. In this case, using the formula for I_3 in Appendix C,

$$\frac{\sigma^2}{\omega_c} \int_0^\infty \omega^2 |\tilde{Y}_1(i\omega)|^2 \, d\omega = \frac{5.57\sigma^2}{f_c T^3}.$$

In another application an even better settling characteristic was obtained (by H. G. Och) with the same circuit complexity by starting with a modification of $W_1(\tau)$ which has no sharp corner at $\tau = T$,

$$W_{1,\text{mod}}(\tau) = \frac{12}{T} \frac{\tau}{T} \left(1 - \frac{\tau}{T}\right)^2 \quad \text{in } 0 \leq \tau \leq T.$$

The approximate transfer function is

$$\tilde{Y}_{1,\text{mod}}(p) = \frac{1 + (29T/640)p}{1 + (57T/128)p + (5T^2/64)p^2 + (31T^3/5376)p^3}.$$

By trial and error it was possible to change these coefficients slightly to obtain the results tabulated below.

t/T	Step response
1	0.9970
1.05	1
1.2	1.0027 (max max)
≥ 1.52	1 ± 0.00043

In this case (I_3 in Appendix C),

$$\frac{\sigma^2}{\omega_c} \int_0^\infty \omega^2 |\tilde{Y}_{1,\text{mod}}(i\omega)|^2 \, d\omega = \frac{9.97\sigma^2}{f_c T^3}.$$

4.6 Approximation to $Y_2(p)$. The simplest and only approximation which has been worked out for this case is

$$\tilde{Y}_2(p) = \frac{1}{1 + (T/2)p + (3T^2/28)p^2 + (T^3/84)p^3}$$

$$= 1 - (1/2)P + (1/7)P^2 - (5/168)P^3 + (13/2352)P^4 - \cdots,$$

where $P = pT$. The impulse response (weighting function) is shown in Fig. 4.7, the step response (settling characteristic) in Fig. 4.8. The step response settles to within 3.2% of unity in $0.9T$ sec. In this case, using the formula for I_3 in Appendix C,

$$\frac{\sigma^2}{\omega_c} \int_0^\infty \omega^4 |\tilde{Y}_2(i\omega)|^2 \, d\omega = \frac{252\sigma^2}{f_c T^5}.$$

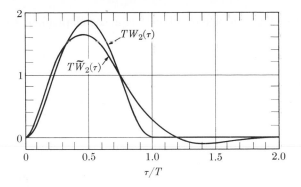

FIG. 4.7. Approximation to impulse response or weighting function $TW_2(\tau)$.

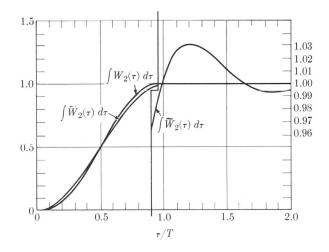

FIG. 4.8. Approximation to step response $\int W_2(\tau)\, d\tau$.

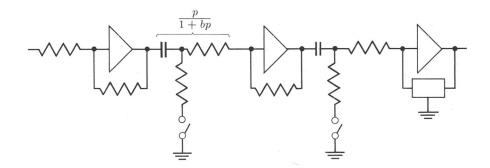

FIG. 4.9. Smoothed second-derivative circuit with protection against overload and with provision for preloading.

For physical realization, a redundant frequency-dependent factor was introduced, so that

$$p^2 \bar{Y}_2(p) = \frac{p}{1 + bp} \frac{p}{1 + 0.265Tp} \frac{1 + bp}{1 + 0.235Tp + 0.0449T^2p^2} ,$$

where $b \approx 0.03T$. The first and second components were realized as input networks (Fig. B.2) and the reciprocal of the third component as a feedback network (Fig. B.5). The complete schematic is shown in Fig. 4.9. The second switch is opened approximately $0.15T$ (that is, $5b$) sec after the first switch is opened but may be opened sooner if a sufficiently close estimate of the initial velocity is incorporated as a D-C voltage in series with the first switch. The settling time of the circuit after the second switch is opened may be effectively shortened if an estimate of the initial acceleration is available. Such an estimate may be incorporated as a D-C voltage in series with the second switch in Fig. 4.9.

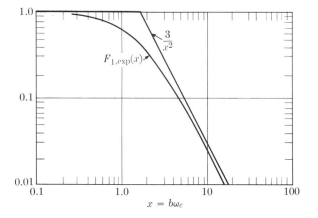

FIG. 4.10. Normalized noise load on second amplifier in Fig. 4.9.

Another function which the redundant frequency-dependent factor has to perform in Fig. 4.9 is to protect the second amplifier from being overloaded with noise. The noise load on the second amplifier, assuming band-limited white noise in the data, is given by

$$\frac{\bar{\sigma}^2_{1,\text{exp}}}{\sigma^2} = \frac{1}{\omega_c} \int_0^{\omega_c} \frac{\omega^2}{1 + b^2\omega^2} \, d\omega$$

$$= \frac{\omega_c^2}{3} F_{1,\text{exp}}(b\omega_c),$$

where

$$F_{1,\text{exp}}(x) = \frac{3}{x^2} \left(1 - \frac{\tan^{-1}x}{x} \right),$$

which is plotted in Fig. 4.10.

4.7 Approximation to $Y_{1,3}(p)$. The transfer function $Y_{1,3}(p)$ corresponds to the weighting function

$$W_{1,3}(\tau) = W_1(\tau) + \frac{T}{2} W_2'(\tau) + \frac{T^2}{10} W_3''(\tau),$$

which has unit area and zero first and second moments. (It is delay-corrected for second-degree inputs.) Thus

$$Y_{1,3}(p) = Y_1(p) + \frac{T}{2} p Y_2(p) + \frac{T^2}{10} p^2 Y_3(p)$$

$$= 1 - \frac{T^3}{84} p^3 + \frac{5T^4}{1008} p^4 - \frac{T^5}{840} p^5 + \frac{T^6}{4752} p^6 - \cdots$$

The simplest stable approximation is

$$\bar{Y}_{1,3}(p) = \frac{1 + a_1 p + a_2 p^2}{1 + b_1 p + b_2 p^2 + b_3 p^3 + b_4 p^4},$$

where

$$a_1 = b_1 = \frac{1990}{4081} T, \qquad a_2 = b_2 = \frac{6316}{61215} T^2,$$

$$b_3 = \frac{1}{84} T^3, \qquad\qquad b_4 = \frac{3475}{4113648} T^4.$$

The fact that the simplest stable approximation is of this degree of complexity should not be surprising. In the first place, in order that the first and second moments be zero, we must have $a_1 = b_1$ and $a_2 = b_2$. If the numerator were any simpler than it is, we would be forced to make $b_2 = 0$, or $b_2 = b_1 = 0$. In either case, the network could not possibly be physically realizable. A necessary condition for physical realizability (that is, stability) is that all coefficients in the denominator, up to and including the term of highest degree, be positive nonzero.* Thus, for realizability reasons alone, the numerator had to be quadratic and the denominator cubic. The reason for the quartic denominator is the same reason that the approximations to $Y_1(p)$ were required to have a denominator at least (preferably just) two degrees higher than the numerator.

Had the transfer functions $Y_1(p)$, $Y_2(p)$, $Y_3(p)$ been approximated independently and then combined, the approximation would have had a denominator of at least the ninth degree and a numerator of the seventh degree. Furthermore, such an approximation would not have preserved the moments of $W_{1,3}(\tau)$ beyond the second.

---

* A network is stable only if its impulse response vanishes in the limit with increasing time; or, equivalently, only if all of the poles of its transfer function have negative nonzero real parts. Now, the product of factors of the form $(p + \alpha)$ or $(p^2 + 2\alpha p + \alpha^2 + \beta^2)$ in which $\alpha > 0$ is a polynomial whose coefficients are all positive nonzero. Hence, this is a necessary condition for stability and realizability.

The approximate transfer function $p\tilde{Y}_{1,3}(p)$ was not intended for analog realization. It was "digitalized" by the "frequency-transformation method" described in the next chapter, and the circled dots in Fig. 4.11 show the sampled-ramp response (settling characteristic) obtained with an IBM-650 digital computer (8-digit accuracy, floating decimal point).

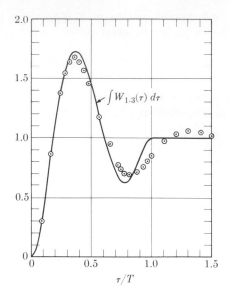

FIG. 4.11. Digitalized approximation to step response $\int W_{1,3}(\tau)\,d\tau$.

The approximate transfer function was subsequently digitalized by the "combined methods of frequency-transformation and of moments," also described in the next chapter, and was then tried out on a Remington-Rand Univac computer with 21-bit accuracy and fixed point. The expected over-all accuracy was not immediately realized for a reason which will be discussed in the next chapter, under "Deadband Effect of Roundoff Errors."

CHAPTER 5

DIGITALIZATION OF ANALOG FILTERS

About a decade ago planning was started on a number of projects involving data-smoothing and prediction in which it was evident that analog computers would not be sufficiently accurate. It was planned, therefore, to use digital computers. In order to meet the immediate need for discrete data-smoothing and prediction schemes, methods of digitalizing continuous data-smoothing and prediction schemes were investigated.

Shortly after this investigation was completed, a theory of optimum discrete data-smoothing and prediction was constructed, and practical discrete data-smoothing schemes based on this theory were developed. It was expected that these discrete schemes would completely supersede those obtained by digitalization of continuous schemes. However, the schemes obtained by digitalization have advantages which outweigh their disadvantages in some situations. The advantages are that they require many fewer memory slots and arithmetical operations for a given nominal smoothing time.† The disadvantages are that the smoothing time is not sharply defined, and the output is more sensitive to roundoff errors.

5.1 Definition and basic objective. The term "digitalization" is used here to mean the conversion of an analog transfer function of the form

$$Y_{\mathrm{An}}(p) = \frac{a_0 + a_1 p + \cdots + a_m p^m}{1 + b_1 p + \cdots + b_n p^n} \qquad (m \leq n) \qquad (5\text{--}1)$$

into an analog transfer function of the (transversal filter) form

$$Y_{\mathrm{Tr}}(q) = \frac{A_0 + A_1 q + \cdots + A_r q^r}{1 + B_1 q + \cdots + B_n q^n} \qquad (q = e^{-p \Delta t}) \qquad (5\text{--}2)$$

and the translation of the latter into the digital computer equation

$$v_k = A_0 u_k + A_1 u_{k-1} + \cdots + A_r u_{k-r} - B_1 v_{k-1} - B_2 v_{k-2} - \cdots - B_n v_{k-n} \tag{5--3}$$

in accordance with Eqs. (1–26) and (1–28).

The basic objective here is, in accordance with Fig. 1.6, to derive a discrete scheme which, when excited with a time series $\{u_k\}$ obtained by sampling a continuous-time function $u(t)$, will generate a time series $\{v_k\}$ which is in some sense equivalent to the time series which would be obtained by sampling the output $v(t)$ of a prescribed continuous scheme which is excited directly by the

---

† The digitalized version of the transfer function $p\widetilde{Y}_{1,3}(p)$ of Section 4.7 requires 11 memory slots, but a nonrecursive discrete scheme with the same smoothing time would have required 51 memory slots.

function $u(t)$. However, since we are dealing here with a prescribed continuous scheme whose transfer function is a rational function of p rather than (as in the lower diagram in Fig. 1.6) of $q = e^{-p\Delta t}$, we cannot secure a strict equivalence of the two output series. Hence, to conform with the results of the analysis in Chapter 2 at least, the emphasis here will be placed on securing the correct moments of the weighting sequence $\{W_j\}$, up to the appropriate order and on securing approximately the same dynamic stability.

5.2 Methods of digitalization. Four methods of digitalization have been investigated. They are: the method of moments, the frequency-transformation method, and two modifications of the method of moments.

These methods will be described, and some of their relative advantages and disadvantages will be noted in the next three sections.

The initial trials of a discrete scheme based on one of these methods revealed an effect which was intolerable. This effect, which came to be called the *dead-band effect*, was discovered by D. C. Borden to be due to roundoff errors. Further investigation showed that it is common to all recursive discrete schemes. This effect will be illustrated, and some remedial measures will be described.

Finally, we will describe a method of digitalization (the *partial-fractions substitution* method) which was actually investigated before the other methods, but which was eventually abandoned. The reason for discussing this method at all is that it is essentially the z-transform method ($z = e^{p\Delta t} = q^{-1}$) which has attracted a great deal of interest.

5.3 Method of moments. The method of moments as a method of digitalization is essentially the same as the method of moments in the derivation of practical analog approximations in Chapter 4. However, there is one important difference in detail with regard to transfer functions of the form $p^r Y_r(p)$ where $Y_r(0) = 1$, and $r > 0$. To derive a practical analog approximation it is not necessary to apply the method of moments to the whole transfer function. In Chapter 4, the method was applied only to the *smoothing part*, $Y_r(p)$. On the other hand, to derive a digitalized approximation it is necessary to apply the method of moments to the whole transfer function. This is because the differencing operator $[(1 - q)/\Delta t]^r$ has nonzero moments of higher than rth-order.†

As an example, consider the approximation to

$$pY_1(p) = p\left(1 - \frac{T}{2}p + \frac{3T^2}{20}p^2 - \cdots\right)$$

of the form

$$Y_{\mathrm{Tr}}(q) = \frac{A_0 + A_1 q}{1 + B_1 q + B_2 q^2} \qquad (q = e^{-p\Delta t}).$$

---

† After $p^r Y_r(p)$ has been digitalized, the resulting $Y_{\mathrm{Tr}}(q)$ should be reexpressed in the form $(1 - q)^r \hat{Y}_{\mathrm{Tr}}(q)$ before programming.

Since, with the expansion of q in powers of p,

$$A_0 + A_1 q = (A_0 + A_1) - (A_1 \Delta t)p + \frac{A_1 \Delta t^2}{2} p^2 - \frac{A_1 \Delta t^3}{6} p^3 + \cdots$$

and

$$1 + B_1 q + B_2 q^2 = (1 + B_1 + B_2) - (B_1 + 2B_2)\, \Delta t\, p$$
$$+ \frac{(B_1 + 4B_2)\, \Delta t^2}{2} p^2 - \cdots,$$

we must satisfy the simultaneous equations

$$A_0 + A_1 = 0,$$
$$1 + B_1 + B_2 = -A_1\, \Delta t,$$
$$1 + B_1 + B_2 + 2h(B_1 + 2B_2) = -hA_1\, \Delta t,$$
$$9(1 + B_1 + B_2) + 30h(B_1 + 2B_2) + 30h^2(B_1 + 4B_2) = -10h^2 A_1\, \Delta t,$$

where $h = \Delta t/T$. Hence

$$A_0 = -A_1 = \frac{1}{\Delta t} \frac{60h^2}{6 + 30h + 25h^2},$$

$$B_1 = -2 \frac{6 + 15h - 20h^2}{6 + 30h + 25h^2},$$

$$B_2 = \frac{6 - 5h^2}{6 + 30h + 25h^2}.$$

A disadvantage of the method of moments is that it requires the series expansion of $Y_{An}(p)$ unless this series is already known as it would be if it were the original basis of the rational function. Another disadvantage is the necessity of solving a set of simultaneous equations.

However, the principal disadvantage of this method is that the resulting scheme is often appreciably less stable than the corresponding analog approximation (to the same number of moments). In the example just worked out, the poles are located at

$$q = \frac{1}{2B_2}\left[-B_1 \pm i\sqrt{4B_2 - B_1^2} \right],$$

hence, at

$$p = \frac{1}{hT}\left[\frac{1}{2} \log_e B_2 \pm i \cos^{-1}\left(-\frac{B_1}{2\sqrt{B_2}} \right) \right],$$

$$= -\frac{2.210 \pm i1.794}{T} \qquad \text{for } h = 0.1,$$

while the poles of the corresponding analog approximation are located at

$$p = -\frac{5 \pm i\sqrt{15}}{2T} = -\frac{2.500 \pm i1.937}{T}.$$

Thus, the decremental exponent for the discrete approximation is about 12% smaller than for the analog approximation.

5.4 Frequency-transformation method. The frequency-transformation method consists simply of the substitution

$$p \rightarrow \frac{2}{\Delta t} \frac{1-q}{1+q}, \qquad q = e^{-p\Delta t}. \tag{5-4}$$

For example, the analog transfer function

$$Y_{\text{An}}(p) = \frac{p}{1 + (T/2)p + (T^2/10)p^2}$$

is thereby converted into

$$Y_{\text{Tr}}(q) = \frac{A_0(1 - q^2)}{1 + B_1 q + B_2 q^2},$$

where

$$A_0 = \frac{1}{\Delta t} \frac{10h^2}{2 + 5h + 5h^2} \qquad \left(h = \frac{\Delta t}{T}\right),$$

$$B_1 = -2\frac{2 - 5h^2}{2 + 5h + 5h^2},$$

$$B_2 = \frac{2 - 5h + 5h^2}{2 + 5h + 5h^2}.$$

Thus, for $h = 0.1$, the poles are located at

$$p = -\frac{2.488 \pm i1.960}{T}.$$

The decremental exponent for this discrete approximation is only $\frac{1}{2}$% smaller than for the analog approximation. This method does not require the series expansion of $Y_{\text{An}}(p)$, it avoids the necessity of solving a set of simultaneous equations, and it results in a closer approximation to the stability of the original analog scheme. However, since

$$\frac{2}{\Delta t} \frac{1-q}{1+q} = \frac{2}{\Delta t} \tanh \frac{p\,\Delta t}{2}$$

$$= p\left[1 - \frac{\Delta t^2}{12} p^2 + \frac{\Delta t^4}{120} p^4 - \cdots\right],$$

the application of the frequency-transformation method to a transfer function of the form $p^r Y_r(p)$, where $Y_r(0) = 1$ and $r > 0$, will usually preserve only the moments up to and including the $(r + 1)$th moment. If this is sufficient, then the frequency-transformation method is, by far, the simplest method of digitalization.

It may be noted that under the frequency-transformation (5–4) the transfer function of the discrete scheme for real frequencies is the transfer function of the analog scheme plotted against a nonlinear frequency scale. If real frequency is denoted by $\omega/(2\pi)$ for the discrete scheme and by $\Omega/(2\pi)$ for the analog scheme then, by (5-4),

$$\Omega = \frac{2}{\Delta t} \tan \frac{\omega \Delta t}{2}$$

or, conversely,

$$\omega = \frac{2}{\Delta t} \tan^{-1} \frac{\Omega \Delta t}{2}.$$

Thus, ω is a multiple-valued function of Ω, in accordance with the fact that the transfer function of any discrete scheme is a periodic function of frequency.

5.5 Modified method of moments. The denominator of $Y_{An}(p)$ may be converted independently of the numerator, either by making the substitution (5-4) and discarding the factor $(1 + q)^n$ which would be introduced into the numerator of $Y_{Tr}(q)$ when the denominator is rationalized, or by factoring and making the substitutions

$$p + \alpha \rightarrow 1 - e^{-\alpha \Delta t}q \qquad (5\text{-}5)$$

$$(p + \alpha + i\beta)(p + \alpha - i\beta) \rightarrow 1 - 2\,e^{-\alpha \Delta t}(\cos \beta\, \Delta t)q + e^{-2\alpha \Delta t}q^2. \qquad (5\text{-}6)$$

In either case, the numerator of $Y_{Tr}(q)$ is determined by the method of moments, with due regard to the predetermined denominator. Note that the degree of the numerator of $Y_{T_1}(q)$, which is r in Eq. (5-2), must now be equal to the order of the highest moment to be preserved, which may well exceed the degree of the denominator.

The use of the substitution (5-4) guarantees the same stability as the frequency-substitution method, while the use of the substitutions (5-5) and (5-6) preserves the stability of the original analog scheme.

5.6 Deadband effect of roundoff errors. In the computer equation

$$v_k = A_0 u_k + A_1 u_{k-1} + \cdots + A_r u_{k-r}$$
$$- B_1 v_{k-1} - B_2 v_{k-2} - \cdots - B_n v_{k-n},$$

let us assume that the quantity

$$A_0 u_k + A_1 u_{k-1} + \cdots + A_r u_{k-r}$$

has become constant and equal to $(1 + B_1 + \cdots + B_n)K$, where $K > 0$. Assuming stability and full-precision computation and storage, the output time series $\{v_k\}$ will eventually become and remain arbitrarily close to K.

Now, let us arbitrarily make all of the stored values of v, namely, v_{k-1}, $v_{k-2}, \cdots, v_{k-n}$, equal to $K - a$, where $a > 0$. Then, v_k will be *computed* as

$$K - a + (1 + B_1 + \cdots + B_n)a.$$

However, if

$$(1 + B_1 + \cdots + B_n)a < \tfrac{1}{2}q_s,$$

where q_s is the *storage quantum* (least significant storable digit), then v_k will be *stored* at the same value as $v_{k-1}, \cdots, v_{k-n}$. Every v, from v_{k-n} on, will have the stored value $K - a$. Similarly, if we arbitrarily make all of the stored values of v equal to $K + a$ where $a > 0$, and if

$$(1 + B_1 + \cdots + B_n)a \leq \tfrac{1}{2}q_s,$$

then, v_k will be *stored* at the same value as $v_{k-1}, \cdots, v_{k-n}$, and every v, from v_{k-n} on, will have the stored value $K + a$. Thus, there is a deadband of width λq_s, where λ is the integral number next below $1/(1 + B_1 + \cdots + B_n)$. The *deadband factor*, λ, is usually very large. In the example worked out under "Method of Moments," we have

$$\frac{1}{1 + B_1 + \cdots + B_n} = \frac{6 + 30h + 25h^2}{60h^2} = 275.4 \qquad \text{for} \qquad h = \tfrac{1}{50},$$

while in the example worked out under "Frequency-Transformation Method," we have

$$\frac{1}{1 + B_1 + \cdots + B_n} = \frac{2 + 5h + 5h^2}{20h^2} = 262.8 \qquad \text{for} \qquad h = \tfrac{1}{50}.$$

5.7 A numerical example. As a simple example, let

$$v_k = 0.04\, u_k + 0.96\, v_{k-1}.$$

If $q_s = 1$, we should get a deadband of width 24. Holding u_k at 100, and starting with v_k at 85, we get

RUN I

u_k	Computed v_k	Stored v_k
100	—	85
100	85.60	86
100	86.56	87
100	87.52	88
100	88.48	88

Starting with v_k at 115, we get

RUN II

u_k	Computed v_k	Stored v_k
100	—	115
100	114.40	114
100	113.44	113
100	112.48	112
100	111.52	112

Starting from the end of Run I, and letting u_k decrease to zero, in unit steps, we get

RUN III

u_k	Computed v_k	Stored v_k
100	88.48	88
99	88.44	88
98	88.40	88
	(20 entries omitted)	(88)
77	87.56	88
76	87.52	88
75	87.48	87
74	86.48	86
	(72 entries omitted)	($u_k + 12$)
1	13.48	13
0	12.48	12
0	11.52	12

5.8 Another numerical example. It is probably worthwhile to consider another numerical example which exhibits what might be called the *momentum effect.* Let

$$v_k = 8.00 + 1.53\, v_{k-1} - 0.61\, v_{k-2}.$$

Starting with $v_{-2} = v_{-1} = 0$, and storing as well as computing to the nearest multiple of 0.01, we get the results shown by the solid dots in Fig. 5.1. (There

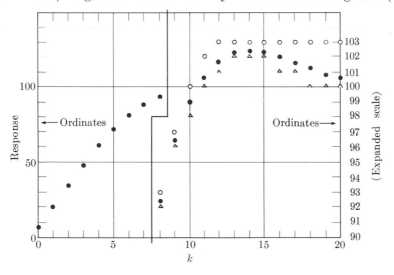

FIG. 5.1. Illustration of deadband effect.

is a deadband of width 0.12, which because of the momentum effect is too small to be manifest in the range of k shown.)

If $q_s = 1$, we should get a deadband of width 12. Thus, if $v_{-2} = v_{-1} = 94$, then v_0 will be computed at 94.48 and stored at 94. On the other hand, if $v_{-2} = v_{-1} = 106$, then v_0 will be computed at 105.52 and stored at 106. However, if $v_{-2} = 93$ and $v_{-1} = 94$, we get

RUN IV

k	Computed v_k	Stored v_k	k	Computed v_k	Stored v_k
-2	—	93	4	98.77	99
-1	—	94	5	99.69	100
0	95.09	95	6	100.61	101
1	96.01	96	7	101.53	102
2	96.93	97	8	102.45	102
3	97.85	98	9	101.84	102

The small change in v_{-2} has enabled v_k to go through $\frac{2}{3}$ of the deadband. This is the *momentum effect*.

If $v_{-2} = 86$ and $v_{-1} = 94$, we get

RUN V

k	Computed v_k	Stored v_k	k	Computed v_k	Stored v_k
-2	—	86	2	103.67	104
-1	—	94	3	104.90	105
0	99.36	99	4	105.21	105
1	102.13	102	5	104.60	105

A much larger change in v_{-2} has not produced enough additional momentum to enable v_k to get completely across the deadband.

If $v_{-2} = 85$ and $v_{-1} = 94$, we get

RUN VI

k	Computed v_k	Stored v_k	k	Computed v_k	Stored v_k
-2	—	85	7	103.99	104
-1	—	94	8	103.07	103
0	99.97	100	9	102.15	102
1	103.66	104	10	101.23	101
2	106.12	106	11	100.31	100
3	106.74	107	12	99.39	99
4	107.05	107	13	98.47	98
5	106.44	106	14	97.55	98
6	104.91	105	15	98.16	98

Here, v_k got far enough on the other side of the deadband to enable it to go through $\frac{2}{3}$ of the deadband in the reverse direction. (Run VI, from $k - 4$ on, is the reflection of Run IV, from $k = -2$ on, about $v_k = 100$.)

5.9 Remedies for the deadband effect. An obvious remedy for the deadband effect is to provide higher precision computation and storage for the v's. Alternatively, the storage for the v's may be of just adequate precision (for purposes other than recursive smoothing) provided that the roundoffs from higher-precision computation are accumulated in an auxiliary storage slot (the piggy bank) from which the overflow is transferred to the v_k-slot at each computation cycle.

Another remedy for the deadband effect may be illustrated first on the first numerical example used. Let us add a *dither* term of amplitude 0.49, at folding frequency, so that

$$v_k = 0.04 \ u_k + 0.96 \ v_{k-1} + (-)^k 0.49.$$

Holding u_k at 100 and starting with v_k at 88, we get

RUN VII

u_k	Computed v_k	Stored v_k
100	—	88
100	88.48 − 0.49	88
100	88.48 + 0.49	89
100	89.44 − 0.49	89
100	89.44 + 0.49	90
	(17 entries omitted)	
100	98.08 + 0.49	99
100	99.04 − 0.49	99
100	99.04 + 0.49	100
100	100.00 − 0.49	100
100	100.00 + 0.49	100

Starting with v_k at 101, we get

RUN VIII

u_k	Computed v_k	Stored v_k
100	—	101
100	100.96 + 0.49	101
100	100.96 − 0.49	100
100	100.00 + 0.49	100
100	100.00 − 0.49	100

Thus, there is no deadband.

However, consider the case of the computer equation

$$v_k = 0.01\ u_k + 0.99\ v_{k-1} + (-)^k 0.49.$$

Holding u_k at 100 and starting with v_k at 99, we get

RUN IX

u_k	Computed v_k	Stored v_k
100	—	99
100	99.01 − 0.49	99
100	99.01 + 0.49	100
100	100.00 − 0.49	100
100	100.00 + 0.49	100

but starting with v_k at 102, we get

RUN X

u_k	Computed v_k	Stored v_k
100	—	102
100	101.98 + 0.49	102
100	101.98 − 0.49	101
100	100.99 + 0.49	101
100	100.99 − 0.49	101

Thus in this case there is an off-center deadband of unit width.

The generalization of the *folding-frequency dither* method of eliminating the deadband effect of roundoff errors is as follows. Program the computer equation as

$$v_k = A_0 u_k + A_1 u_{k-1} + \cdots + A_r u_{k-r}$$
$$- B_1 v_{k-1} - B_2 v_{k-2} - \cdots - B_n v_{k-n} + (-)^k D,$$

with dither term $(-)^k D$, and take

$$D = \tfrac{1}{2} q_s - q_a,$$

where q_s is the *storage quantum* and q_a is the *arithmetical quantum*. This will eliminate the deadband completely if

$$q_a < (1 + B_1 \cdots + B_n) q_s,$$

but it will leave an off-center deadband of width q_s if

$$q_a = (1 + B_1 + \cdots + B_n) q_s.$$

The latter situation may be avoided by adding another place to the arithmetical accuracy.

It is also of some interest to see the effect of dither on the settling characteristic shown in Fig. 5.1 when $q_s = 1$. Without dither we get

RUN XI

k	Computed v_k	Stored v_k	k	Computed v_k	Stored v_k
-2	—	0	7	88.01	88
-1	—	0	8	93.23	93
0	8.00	8	9	96.61	97
1	20.24	20	10	99.68	100
2	33.72	34	11	101.83	102
3	47.82	48	12	103.06	103
4	60.70	61	13	103.37	103
5	72.05	72	14	102.76	103
6	80.95	81			

These are shown by the circles in Fig. 5.1. With dither we get

RUN XII

k	Computed v_k	Stored v_k	k	Computed v_k	Stored v_k
-2	—	0	10	$98.76 - 0.49$	98
-1	—	0	11	$99.38 + 0.49$	100
0	$8.00 - 0.49$	8	12	$101.22 - 0.49$	101
1	$20.24 + 0.49$	21	13	$101.53 + 0.49$	102
2	$35.25 - 0.49$	35	14	$102.45 - 0.49$	102
3	$48.74 + 0.49$	49	15	$101.84 + 0.49$	102
4	$61.62 - 0.49$	61	16	$101.84 - 0.49$	101
5	$71.44 + 0.49$	72	17	$100.31 + 0.49$	101
6	$80.95 - 0.49$	80	18	$100.92 - 0.49$	100
7	$86.48 + 0.49$	87	19	$99.39 + 0.49$	100
8	$92.31 - 0.49$	92	20	$100.00 - 0.49$	100
9	$95.69 + 0.49$	96	21	$100.00 + 0.49$	100

These are shown by the triangles in Fig. 5.1.

R. G. Rausch at Bell Telephone Laboratories has found that random noise in the data may often be relied upon to substantially eliminate the deadband effect, without resorting to intentional dither. (The inadvertent omission of simulated noise in testing a rocket guidance program on the eve of its scheduled use gave rise to some frantic transcontinental telephone calls.)

5.10 Partial-fractions substitution method. This method is essentially the so-called *z-transform* method, although the discussion here does not require any familiarity with *z*-transform theory. (The *z* in *z*-transform theory is the reciprocal of our *q* and is on that account occasionally referred to as an *advance operator*.)

A common method of determining the impulse response or weighting function corresponding to an analog transfer function of the form

$$Y_{An}(p) = \frac{a_0 + a_1 p + \cdots + a_m p^m}{1 + b_1 p + \cdots + b_n p^n} \qquad (m \leq n)$$

is to expand the transfer function into partial fractions of the form

$$\frac{1}{(p + \alpha)^\nu},$$

where α may be complex (with positive real part) and ν is a positive integer. Each such partial fraction (aside from the constant multiplier which occurs with it) contributes a term of the form

$$\frac{t^{\nu - 1}}{(\nu - 1)!} e^{-\alpha t}$$

to the impulse response. If α is complex, there will be two such terms with conjugate-complex exponentials and conjugate-complex multipliers so that their contribution to the impulse response is necessarily real. Usually $\nu = 1$, whether α is real or complex. Let us assume, then, that

$$Y_{An}(p) = \frac{1}{p + \alpha},$$

where α may be complex, so that the impulse response is simply $e^{-\alpha t}$. Correspondingly, let

$$Y_{Tr}(q) = \frac{1}{1 - \gamma q},$$

for which the computer equation is

$$v_k = u_k + \gamma v_{k-1}.$$

Letting $v_k = 0$ for $k < 0$ and $u_k = 0$ except $u_0 = 1$, the impulse response of the discrete scheme is simply γ^k for $k \geq 0$. This is $e^{-\alpha t}$ for $t = k\,\Delta t$, if $\gamma = e^{-\alpha \Delta t}$. Hence, the partial-fractions substitution formula is

$$\frac{1}{p + \alpha} \rightarrow \frac{1}{1 - \gamma q} \qquad (\gamma = e^{-\alpha \Delta t}) \tag{5-7}$$

for simple poles.

On the comparatively rare occasions when we might have to deal with multiple poles, the appropriate substitution formulas may be obtained from the one for simple poles by taking partial derivatives with respect to α. Thus, for example,

$$\frac{1}{(p + \alpha)^2} \rightarrow \frac{\Delta t\,\gamma q}{(1 - \gamma q)^2}, \qquad \frac{1}{(p + \alpha)^3} \rightarrow \frac{(\Delta t)^2 \gamma q(1 + \gamma q)}{2(1 - \gamma q)^3} \qquad (\gamma = e^{-\alpha \Delta t}).$$

These substitution formulas comprise the essentials of z-transform theory (Truxal (1955) p. 511, Table 9.1).

From the equation $\gamma = e^{-\alpha \Delta t}$ it will be readily seen that, just as $\mathrm{Re}[\alpha] > 0$ (or $\alpha = 0$ for integration) is the stability criterion in the p-plane, so $|\gamma^{-1}| > 1$ (or $\gamma = 1$ for summation) is the stability criterion in the q-plane. In other words, $Y_{\mathrm{An}}(p)$ must be analytic on, and to the right of, the imaginary axis in the p-plane (excluding $p = 0$); $Y_{\mathrm{Tr}}(q)$ must be analytic on, and within, the unit circle in the q-plane (excluding $q = 1$).

Examining the substitution formula (5–7), we find that

(1) It is not dimensionally homogeneous, and

(2) As $\Delta t \to 0$, the right-hand member is asymptotic to $1/(p + \alpha) \Delta t$ rather than $1/(p + \alpha)$.

Both of these discrepancies can be eliminated by modifying the substitution formula to read

$$\frac{1}{p + \alpha} \to \frac{\Delta t}{1 - \gamma q}. \tag{5–8}$$

However, the elimination of these discrepancies is not important. A more important discrepancy of the substitution formula (5–7) is the fact that the two members of the formula are not equal for $p = 0$ so that its use will not ordinarily preserve even the zeroth moment of the weighting function.

In the case of a $Y_{\mathrm{An}}(p)$ with a root of multiplicity m at $p = 0$, the preservation of the zeroth to $(m - 1)$th moments of the weighting function, which are zero, is usually important. It may be achieved by separating out a factor p^m for independent treatment (with, for example, the substitution formula $p \to (1 - q)/(\Delta t)$ and applying the substitution formula (5–7) or (5–8) to the remainder of $Y_{\mathrm{An}}(p)$. The mth moment may then be adjusted to any prescribed nonzero value by subsequent introduction of a suitable constant factor into $Y_{\mathrm{Tr}}(q)$. Alternatively, if $m = 1$, the preservation of the zeroth moment may be achieved by using the substitution formula

$$\frac{1}{p + \alpha} \to \frac{(1 - \gamma)/\alpha}{1 - \gamma q}. \tag{5–9}$$

Other substitution formulas have been improvised for the treatment of somewhat more general cases of $Y_{\mathrm{An}}(p)$ in which the moments to be preserved went beyond the lowest order of nonzero value. Such improvisations are clearly inefficient and unsatisfactory. The substitution method has been abandoned in favor of the other methods of digitalization described above.

It should be noted that, while the partial-fractions substitution method (including the z-transform method) is not suited to the digitalization of analog data-smoothing and prediction schemes, the substitution formula (5–7), which is basically the z-transform theory, is well suited to the analysis of the stability of feedback (or automatic control) loops which are partly analog and partly

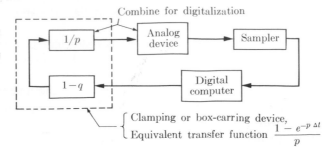

Combine for digitalization

Clamping or box-carring device,
Equivalent transfer function $\dfrac{1 - e^{-p\,\Delta t}}{p}$

FIG. 5.2. A computation loop which is partly analog and partly digital.

digital computer. This is because we are concerned, in the latter case, with the digitalization of an analog scheme which is excited with discrete-time data (see Fig. 5.2). In the case of data-smoothing and prediction, we are concerned with the digitalization of an analog scheme which is excited with continuous-time data (with output sampling as in Fig. 5.3), although the digitalized scheme will of course be excited with discrete-time data and will not need output sampling. (See Fig. 5.4 and compare Figs. 5.3 and 5.4 with Fig. 1.6.)

FIG. 5.3. System to be digitalized.

FIG. 5.4. Digitalized system.

In this connection it may be noted that the loop transfer function, after digitalization of the analog part of the loop as shown in Fig. 5.2, will be a rational function of q. This loop transfer function may then be converted to a rational function of p by making the substitution

$$q \to \frac{1 - (\Delta t/2)p}{1 + (\Delta t/2)p},$$

or, more simply, the substitution

$$q \to \frac{1 - p}{1 + p}.$$

The usual Nyquist diagram may then be used to examine the stability of the system.

If the digital computer takes a computing time in each computation cycle, which is between $(r - 1)\,\Delta t$ and $r\,\Delta t$, an extra factor of q^r should be appended to the loop transfer function to account for the delay.

CHAPTER 6

OPTIMIZATION—DISCRETE SCHEMES

6.1 Introductory remarks. In this chapter we will derive the optimum weighting sequences for discrete-time data in the presence of Markov noise. In a sense, these derivations are similar to those in Chapter 3. However, there are important differences in detail, aside from the fact that we must now deal with sums instead of integrals. In the case of continuous time it was convenient in the optimization procedure to separate differentiations from smoothings. In the discrete case, the separation of differencings from smoothings is not convenient because the differencing operator $[(1 - q)/\Delta t]^m$ has nonzero moments of higher than mth order; and although it may be recalled from the last section in Chapter 1 that an mth-order *differencer* may be regarded as a cascade (or tandem) combination of an mth-order *differentiator* and a smoother, the transfer function of this smoother is unfortunately not a rational function of $q = e^{-p\Delta t}$. Hence, the discrete schemes derived here are the counterparts of the $W_r^{(r)}(\tau)$ in Fig. 2.3, rather than the $W_r(\tau)$ in Fig. 2.2. However, the notation used here bears no relation to the notation used in Chapter 2.

The optimization procedure used here is analytically manageable only for Markov noise (of which white noise is a special case).

6.2 Case I. Discrete version of $W_0(\tau)$. We are concerned here with the minimization of var $\{v\}$ where

$$v_k = \sum_{r=0}^{n} W_r u_{k-r} \tag{6-1}$$

and the u's are equispaced samples from a stationary random process. The minimization is to be performed with respect to the weights W_r and is to be subject to the constraint

$$\sum_{r=0}^{n} W_r = 1. \tag{6-2}$$

Now,

$$\text{var } \{v\} = \text{ave } \{v^2\} = \sum_{r=0}^{n} \sum_{s=0}^{n} W_r W_s C_{rs},$$

where

$$C_{rs} = \text{ave } \{u_{k-r} u_{k-s}\} - C[(r - s) \Delta t]$$

and $C(\tau)$ is the autocovariance of the stationary random process for time shift

85

(lag or lead) τ. Then,

$$\frac{\text{var } \{v\}}{\text{var } \{u\}} = \sum_{r=0}^{n} \sum_{s=0}^{n} \rho_{rs} W_r W_s, \tag{6-3}$$

where the ρ_{rs} are the autocorrelation coefficients (normalized autocovariances).

By elementary calculus of variations, the weights W_r should satisfy the equations

$$\sum_{s=0}^{n} \rho_{rs} W_s = \alpha \qquad (r = 0, 1, \ldots, n), \tag{6-4}$$

where α is a constant (Lagrangian multiplier) to be determined ultimately by the constraint (6–2). If the ρ_{rs} are regarded as elements of a matrix $[\rho]$, the solutions of (6–4) are

$$W_r = \alpha \sum_{s=0}^{n} \nu_{rs}, \tag{6-5}$$

where the ν_{rs} are the elements of the reciprocal matrix

$$[\nu] = [\rho]^{-1}. \tag{6-6}$$

By Eqs. (6–2) and (6–5),

$$\alpha = \frac{1}{\sum_{r=0}^{n} \sum_{s=0}^{n} \nu_{rs}}. \tag{6-7}$$

Substituting Eqs. (6–4) and (6–5) into Eq. (6–3), we get

$$\frac{\text{var } \{v\}}{\text{var } \{u\}} = \alpha^2 \sum_{r=0}^{n} \sum_{s=0}^{n} \nu_{rs},$$

whence, by Eq. (6–7),

$$\frac{\text{var } \{v\}}{\text{var } \{u\}} = \alpha. \tag{6-8}$$

For Markov noise, the autocorrelation (normalized autocovariance) function is

$$\rho(\tau) = \frac{C(\tau)}{C(0)} = e^{-\omega_c |\tau|}. \tag{6-9}$$

This corresponds to the power spectrum assumed in Example I, Chapter 3. Hence, if

$$\rho = e^{-\omega_c \Delta t},$$

then

$$[\rho] = \begin{vmatrix} 1 & \rho & \rho^2 & \cdots & \rho^n \\ \rho & 1 & \rho & \cdots & \rho^{n-1} \\ \rho^2 & \rho & 1 & \cdots & \rho^{n-2} \\ \vdots & & & & \vdots \\ \rho^n & \rho^{n-1} & \rho^{n-2} & \cdots & 1 \end{vmatrix}. \tag{6-10}$$

The reciprocal matrix $[\nu]$ is one in which

(1) the element at each end of the main diagonal is

$$\frac{1}{1 - \rho^2},$$

(2) all of the other elements in the main diagonal are

$$\frac{1 + \rho^2}{1 - \rho^2},$$

(3) all of the elements adjacent to the main diagonal are

$$- \frac{\rho}{1 - \rho^2},$$

(4) all other elements are zero.

Hence, by Eqs. (6–7) and (6–8),

$$\frac{\text{var } \{v\}}{\text{var } \{u\}} = \alpha = \frac{1 + \rho}{(n + 1) - (n - 1)\rho}, \qquad (6\text{–}11)$$

and by Eq. (6–5)

$$W_0 = W_n = \frac{1}{(n + 1) - (n - 1)\rho},$$

$$(6\text{–}12)$$

$$W_r = \frac{1 - \rho}{(n + 1) - (n - 1)\rho} \qquad (r = 1, 2, \ldots, n - 1).$$

If we replace these optimum weights by

$$\widetilde{W}_r = \frac{1}{n + 1} \qquad (r = 0, 1, \ldots, n) \qquad (6\text{–}13)$$

as if $\rho = 0$ (that is, *as if* $\omega_c \to \infty$), then by Eq. (6–3)

$$\frac{\text{var } \{v\}}{\text{var } \{u\}} = \frac{(n + 1) - 2\rho - (n + 1)\rho^2 + 2\rho^{n+2}}{(n + 1)^2 (1 - \rho)^2}. \qquad (6\text{–}14)$$

It will be noted that both Eqs. (6–11) and (6–14) not only approach the same value of $1/(n + 1)$ as $\omega_c \to \infty$, but they also approach the same value of 1 as $\omega_c \to 0$. The situation here, for intermediate values of ω_c, is very much like that in the case of Example I and Fig. 3.1. From the standpoint of the variance ratio, the optimum weights (6–12) offer very little advantage over the weights (6–13).

6.3 Case II. Discrete version of $W_1^{(1)}(\tau)$. Let us now replace the constraint (6–2) in the preceding case by a pair of constraints (analogous to Eqs. (2–10) for $m = n = 1$) on the zeroth and first moments,

$$\sum_{r=0}^{n} W_r = 0, \qquad \Delta t \sum_{r=0}^{n} r W_r = -1. \qquad (6\text{–}15)$$

Using matrix notation for convenience, the problem here is to minimize the variance ratio (6–3), now written as

$$\frac{\text{var } \{v\}}{\text{var } \{u\}} = [W]_t[\rho][W], \tag{6-16}$$

under the constraint

$$[r]_t[W] = [\mu], \tag{6-17}$$

where

$$[W] = \begin{bmatrix} W_0 \\ W_1 \\ W_2 \\ \vdots \\ W_n \end{bmatrix};$$

$[\rho]$ is the autocorrelation matrix; $[W]_t$ is the transpose of $[W]$; $[r]_t$ is the transpose of

$$[r] = \begin{bmatrix} 1 & 0 \\ 1 & 1 \\ 1 & 2 \\ \vdots & \vdots \\ 1 & n \end{bmatrix};$$

and

$$[\mu] = -\frac{1}{\Delta t} \begin{bmatrix} 0 \\ 1 \end{bmatrix}.$$

By elementary calculus of variations, the weights W_r should satisfy the matrix equation

$$[\rho][W] = [r] [\alpha], \tag{6-18}$$

where the matrix (Lagrangian multiplier)

$$[\alpha] = \begin{bmatrix} \alpha_0 \\ \alpha_1 \end{bmatrix}$$

is to be determined ultimately by the constraint (6–17). The solution of Eq. (6–18) may be expressed in the form

$$[W] = [\nu][r][\alpha] \tag{6-19}$$

where $[\nu]$ is, as in Eq. (6–6), the reciprocal autocorrelation matrix. Substituting Eq. (6–19) into Eq. (6–17), we get

$$[r]_t[\nu][r][\alpha] = [\mu]. \tag{6-20}$$

Then,

$$[\alpha] = [\lambda][\mu], \tag{6-21}$$

where

$$[\lambda] = [[r]_t[\nu][r]]^{-1}. \tag{6-22}$$

Substituting Eq. (6–19) into Eq. (6–16) and noting that $[\nu]$ like $[\rho]$ is symmetrical about the main diagonal, so that $[\nu]_t = [\nu]$, we get

$$\frac{\text{var } \{v\}}{\text{var } \{u\}} = [\alpha]_t[r]_t[\nu][r][\alpha].$$

Hence by Eq. (6–20)

$$\frac{\text{var } \{v\}}{\text{var } \{u\}} = [\alpha]_t[\mu], \tag{6–23}$$

and by Eq. (6–21), noting that $[\lambda]_t = [\lambda]$,

$$\frac{\text{var } \{v\}}{\text{var } \{u\}} = [\mu]_t[\lambda][\mu]. \tag{6–24}$$

Substituting Eq. (6–21) into Eq. (6–19), we get

$$[W] = [\nu][r][\lambda][\mu]. \tag{6–25}$$

In Eqs. (6–22), (6–24), and (6–25) we need first to determine the product $[\nu][r]$. The matrix $[\nu]$ was described in the preceding section, and the matrix $[r]$ was defined earlier in this section. Thus $[\nu][r]$ is a matrix of $(n + 1)$ rows and 2 columns, in which

(1) the top row is

$$\frac{1}{1 + \rho}, \qquad -\frac{\rho}{1 - \rho^2},$$

(2) the next $(n - 1)$ rows are

$$\frac{1 - \rho}{1 + \rho}, \qquad r\frac{1 - \rho}{1 + \rho},$$

where $r = 1, 2, \ldots, (n - 1)$,
(3) the bottom row is

$$\frac{1}{1 + \rho}, \qquad \frac{n - (n - 1)\rho}{1 - \rho^2}.$$

Hence, we may write

$$[\nu][r] = \frac{1 - \rho}{1 + \rho}[r] + \frac{\rho}{1 + \rho}[s], \tag{6–26}$$

where $[s]$ is a matrix of $(n + 1)$ rows and 2 columns, in which

(1) the top row is

$$1, \qquad -\frac{1}{1 - \rho},$$

(2) the next $(n - 1)$ rows are

$$0, \qquad 0,$$

(3) the bottom row is

$$1, \qquad n + \frac{1}{1 - \rho}.$$

To make use of Eq. (6–26) in Eq. (6–22), we need the product

$$[r]_t[r] = \begin{bmatrix} \sum_0^n 1 & \sum_0^n r \\[2ex] \sum_0^n r & \sum_0^n r^2 \end{bmatrix},$$

of which the elements are given explicitly by the formulas in Appendix D. We need also the product

$$[r]_t[s] = \begin{bmatrix} 2 & n \\[1ex] n & n^2 + \dfrac{n}{1-\rho} \end{bmatrix}.$$

Then in terms of

$$k = \frac{1-\rho}{1+\rho}, \tag{6–27}$$

we have

$$[r]_t[\nu][r] = \begin{bmatrix} 1 + kn & \dfrac{n}{2}(1 + kn) \\[2ex] \dfrac{n}{2}(1 + kn) & \dfrac{(3 - k^2)n}{12k} + \dfrac{n^2}{2} + \dfrac{kn^3}{3} \end{bmatrix}.$$

Hence by Eq. (6–22), the elements of the matrix $[\lambda]$ are

$$\lambda_{11} = \frac{1}{G}[2(1 + kn)(1 + 2kn) + (1 - k^2)],$$

$$\lambda_{12} = \lambda_{21} = -\frac{6}{G}k(1 + kn),$$

$$\lambda_{22} = \frac{12}{G}\frac{k(1 + kn)}{n},$$

where

$$G = (1 + kn)[(1 + kn)(2 + kn) + (1 - k^2)].$$

Then by Eq. (6–24),

$$\frac{\text{var }\{v\}}{\text{var }\{u\}} = \frac{1}{\Delta t^2}\frac{12k}{n[(1 + kn)(2 + kn) + (1 - k^2)]}, \tag{6–28}$$

and by Eq. (6–25),

$$W_0 = -W_n = \frac{3}{\Delta t}\frac{(1 + k)[1 + k(n - 1)]}{n[(1 + kn)(2 + kn) + (1 - k^2)]}, \tag{6–29}$$

$$W_r = \frac{6}{\Delta t}\frac{k^2(n - 2r)}{n[(1 + kn)(2 + kn) + (1 - k^2)]} \qquad (r = 1, 2, \ldots, n - 1).$$

From the standpoint of the variance ratio, these optimum weights offer very little advantage over the weights (*as if* $\omega_c \to \infty$)

$$\widetilde{W}_r = \frac{6}{\Delta t} \frac{n - 2r}{n(n+1)(n+2)} \qquad (r = 0, 1, \ldots, n). \qquad (6\text{--}30)$$

In the early 1940's, when the need for discrete schemes had not yet arisen, G. R. Stibitz undertook to determine numerically the optimum weighting function for "differentiated" noise, using actual tracking error data obtained by tracking airplanes with a radar equipped with a bore-sight movie camera. The result was regarded at that time as a good confirmation of Eq. (3–21). In retrospect, however, the result may be more properly regarded as a confirmation of the cumulative sums of the weights described in Eq. (6–29),

$$\Delta t \sum_{r=0}^{r=h} W_r = \frac{3}{n} \frac{(1-k)[1+k(n+1)] + 2k^2(1+h)(n-h)}{(1+kn)(2+kn) + (1-k^2)},$$

$$(h = 0, 1, \ldots, n-1).$$

With $k = 1$, this is the formula for $W_1(h\,\Delta t)$ given in the next chapter.

6.4 Case III. Discrete version of $W_2^{(2)}(\tau)$.

If the constraints (6–15) in the preceding case are replaced by

$$\sum_{r=0}^{n} W_r = 0,$$

$$\sum_{r=0}^{n} rW_r = 0,$$

$$(\Delta t)^2 \sum_{r=0}^{n} r^2 W_r = 2,$$

(analogous to Eqs. (2–10) for $m = n = 2$), Eq. (6–17) still holds provided that

$$[r] = \begin{bmatrix} 1 & 0 & 0 \\ 1 & 1 & 1 \\ 1 & 2 & 4 \\ \vdots & \vdots & \vdots \\ 1 & n & n^2 \end{bmatrix} \qquad \text{and} \qquad [\mu] = \frac{2}{(\Delta t)^2} \begin{bmatrix} 0 \\ 0 \\ 1 \end{bmatrix}.$$

Equation (6–18) also still holds provided that

$$[\alpha] = \begin{bmatrix} \alpha_0 \\ \alpha_1 \\ \alpha_2 \end{bmatrix}.$$

Thus, Eqs. (6–22), (6–24), and (6–25) still hold.

It is not difficult to determine the product $[\nu][r]$ and the product $[r]_t[\nu]|r]$, but it becomes very difficult to invert the latter to get $[\lambda]$. This difficulty does not arise in the discrete versions of Eqs. (3–37) and (3–38), but the resulting formulas for the weighting sequences are too complicated for practical use. We will, therefore, proceed under the assumption that $\rho = 0$, so that Eqs. (6–22), (6–24), and (6–25) simplify to

$$[\lambda] = [[r]_t[r]]^{-1}, \tag{6-31}$$

$$\frac{\text{var } \{v\}}{\text{var } \{u\}} = [\mu]_t[\lambda][\mu], \tag{6-32}$$

$$[W] = [r][\lambda][\mu]. \tag{6-33}$$

Note that we will not need all of the elements in $[\lambda]$, but only those in the third column.

Now, we have the product

$$[r]_t[r] = \begin{bmatrix} \sum\limits_{0}^{n} 1 & \sum\limits_{0}^{n} r & \sum\limits_{0}^{n} r^2 \\[2mm] \sum\limits_{0}^{n} r & \sum\limits_{0}^{n} r^2 & \sum\limits_{0}^{n} r^3 \\[2mm] \sum\limits_{0}^{n} r^2 & \sum\limits_{0}^{n} r^3 & \sum\limits_{0}^{n} r^4 \end{bmatrix}$$

of which the elements are given explicitly by the formulas in Appendix D. Hence, by Eq. (6–31),

$$\lambda_{11} = \frac{3(3n^2 + 3n + 2)}{(n + 1)(n + 2)(n + 3)},$$

$$\lambda_{12} = \lambda_{21} = -\frac{18(2n + 1)}{(n + 1)(n + 2)(n + 3)},$$

$$\lambda_{13} = \lambda_{31} = \frac{30}{(n + 1)(n + 2)(n + 3)},$$

$$\lambda_{22} = \frac{12(2n + 1)(8n - 3)}{(n - 1)n(n + 1)(n + 2)(n + 3)},$$

$$\lambda_{23} = \lambda_{32} = -\frac{180}{(n - 1)(n + 1)(n + 2)(n + 3)},$$

$$\lambda_{33} = \frac{180}{(n - 1)n(n + 1)(n + 2)(n + 3)}.$$

Then by Eq. (6–32), we get

$$\frac{\text{var } \{v\}}{\text{var } \{u\}} = \frac{4\lambda_{33}}{(\Delta t)^4} = \frac{1}{(\Delta t)^4} \frac{720}{(n - 1)n(n + 1)(n + 2)(n + 3)}, \tag{6-34}$$

and by Eq. (6–33),

$$W_r = \frac{2}{(\Delta t)^2} (\lambda_{13} + \lambda_{23} r + \lambda_{33} r^2)$$

$$\hspace{3cm} (6\text{–}35)$$

$$= \frac{60}{(\Delta t)^2} \frac{n(n-1) - 6nr + 6r^2}{(n-1)n(n+1)(n+2)(n+3)} \qquad (r = 0, 1, \ldots, n).$$

6.5 Bandlimited white noise. While bandlimited white noise is not a special case of Markov noise, it will be noted that if bandlimited white noise with cutoff frequency f_c is sampled at a frequency of $2f_c$ or an integral submultiple of $2f_c$, the samples will be uncorrelated. Hence, if the sampling frequency is $2f_c$, the weights (6–13), (6–30), and (6–35), are optimum.

If the sampling frequency is $2f_c/n$, where n is an integer, the variance of the output noise will be n times as large due to "aliasing" or "folding" as described in Section 10.8. In practical situations involving data transmission over long distances, a reduction in the quantity (or rate) of data transmission might be worth the penalty of enhanced output noise. However, this penalty may be avoided at the price of "prefiltering and decimating" as described in Section 10.13.

6.6 Nonstationary Noise. The optimization procedure used here may be carried out numerically in cases where it is not analytically manageable, including cases of nonstationary noise (see Friedland, 1958, and Musa, 1963).

CHAPTER 7

DISCRETE WEIGHTING SEQUENCES OPTIMIZED FOR
BANDLIMITED WHITE NOISE

This chapter is the discrete counterpart of the Section 3.5. It gives the discrete weighting sequences which are optimum for bandlimited white noise with cutoff frequency $f_c = 1/(2\,\Delta t)$, where Δt is the sampling interval. In addition, it gives the corresponding output/input variance ratios and some of the moments of the weighting sequences.

In keeping with the notation used in Fig. 2.3, the weighting sequences (6–13), (6–30), and (6–35) are denoted here by $W_0(h\,\Delta t)$, $W_1^{(1)}(h\,\Delta t)$, and $W_2^{(2)}(h\,\Delta t)$, respectively. However, the superscripts here stand for orders of divided differences rather than for orders of derivatives, and divided differences are implicitly defined in such a way that

$$\lim_{\Delta t \to 0} \frac{W_r^{(r)}(h\,\Delta t)}{\Delta t} = W_r^{(r)}(\tau)$$

rather than $(1/r!)W_r^{(r)}(\tau)$. The argument $h\,\Delta t$ corresponds to the age-of-data variable τ in the notation of Fig. 2.3.

Thus, for $h = 0, 1, 2, \ldots, n$, the weighting sequences are

$$W_0(h\,\Delta t) = \frac{1}{n+1},$$

$$W_1^{(1)}(h\,\Delta t) = \frac{6}{\Delta t}\,\frac{n - 2h}{n(n+1)(n+2)},$$

$$W_2^{(2)}(h\,\Delta t) = \frac{60}{(\Delta t)^2}\,\frac{n(n-1) - 6nh + 6h^2}{(n-1)n(n+1)(n+2)(n+3)},$$

$$W_3^{(3)}(h\,\Delta t) = \frac{840}{(\Delta t)^3}\,\frac{(n-3)!}{(n+4)!}$$
$$\times\,[n(n-1)(n-2) - 2(6n^2 - 3n + 2)h + 30nh^2 - 20h^3],$$

$$W_4^{(4)}(h\,\Delta t) = \frac{15120}{(\Delta t)^4}\,\frac{(n-4)!}{(n+5)!}[n(n-1)(n-2)(n-3)$$
$$-\,10n(2n^2 - 3n + 5)h + 10(9n^2 - 3n + 5)h^2$$
$$-\,140nh^3 + 70h^4].$$

The output/input variance ratios are obtained as the squares, summed with

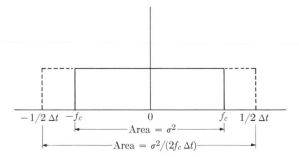

FIG. 7.1. Approximate method of accounting for sample-to-sample correlation when $f_c < 1/(2 \, \Delta t)$.

respect to h, with the help of the formulas in Appendix D. For $W_r^{(r)}(h \, \Delta t)$ they are

r	$\bar{\sigma}_r^2/\sigma^2$
0	$\dfrac{1}{n+1}$
1	$\dfrac{12}{(\Delta t)^2} \dfrac{(n-1)!}{(n+2)!}$
2	$\dfrac{720}{(\Delta t)^4} \dfrac{(n-2)!}{(n+3)!}$
3	$\dfrac{100800}{(\Delta t)^6} \dfrac{(n-3)!}{(n+4)!}$
4	$\dfrac{25401600}{(\Delta t)^8} \dfrac{(n-4)!}{(n+5)!}$

The weighting sequences given above are very nearly optimum even when $f_c < 1/(2 \, \Delta t)$ provided that, as in Chapter 3,

$$\frac{\bar{\sigma}_r^2}{\sigma^2} \ll \frac{\omega_c^{2r}}{2r+1}.$$

However, since the output variances are proportional to the *density* of the input power spectrum (the pass band being narrower than the spectrum), the output/input variance ratios given in the table should be multiplied by $1/(2f_c \, \Delta t)$ in accordance with Fig. 7.1. This effectively takes account of noise sample-to-sample correlation in a painless, but slightly pessimistic, way. If we were then to let $\Delta t \to 0$ keeping f_c fixed (and $n \to \infty$, keeping $n \, \Delta t = T$ fixed), we would get the output/input variance ratios given by Eq. (3–47).

The first five moments (zeroth to fourth) of $W_0(h \, \Delta t)$ are:

$$1, \quad \frac{n}{2} \, \Delta t, \quad \frac{n(2n+1)}{6} \, (\Delta t)^2, \quad \frac{n^2(n+1)}{4} \, (\Delta t)^3, \quad \frac{n(2n+1)(3n^2+3n-1)}{30} \, (\Delta t)^4.$$

Those of $W_1^{(1)}(h\,\Delta t)$ are:

$$0, \quad -1, \quad -n\,\Delta t, \quad -\frac{(3n-1)(3n+2)}{10}(\Delta t)^2, \quad -\frac{n(4n^2+3n-2)}{5}(\Delta t)^3.$$

Those of $W_2^{(2)}(h\,\Delta t)$ are:

$$0, \quad 0, \quad 2, \quad 3n\,\Delta t, \quad \frac{2(12n^2+3n-5)}{7}(\Delta t)^2.$$

Those of $W_3^{(3)}(h\,\Delta t)$ are:

$$0, \quad 0, \quad 0, \quad -6, \quad -12n\,\Delta t.$$

Those of $W_4^{(4)}(h\,\Delta t)$ are:

$$0, \quad 0, \quad 0, \quad 0, \quad 24.$$

In practice, it is better from the standpoint of computational accuracy to separate differencing operations from discrete smoothing operations. Thus, the optimum *smoothing sequence* for divided first differences is

$$W_1(h\,\Delta t) = 6\frac{(1+h)(n-h)}{n(n+1)(n+2)}.$$

The optimum smoothing sequence for divided second differences is

$$W_2(h\,\Delta t) = 30\frac{(1+h)(2+h)(n-1-h)(n-h)}{(n-1)n(n+1)(n+2)(n+3)}.$$

The optimum smoothing sequence for divided third differences is

$$W_3(h\,\Delta t) =$$

$$140\frac{(n-3)!}{(n+4)!}(1+h)(2+h)(3+h)(n-2-h)(n-1-h)(n-h).$$

The optimum smoothing sequence for divided fourth differences is

$$W_4(h\,\Delta t) = 630\frac{(n-4)!}{(n+5)!}(1+h)(2+h)(3+h)(4+h)$$

$$(n-3-h)(n-2-h)(n-1-h)(n-h).$$

These formulas evidently follow a simpler pattern than the formulas for the $W_r^{(r)}(h\,\Delta t)$ given earlier in this chapter. In fact, each of the $W_r^{(r)}(h\,\Delta t)$ was obtained from the corresponding $W_r(h\,\Delta t)$ by the use of the equation

$$W_r^{(s+1)}(h\,\Delta t) = \frac{1}{\Delta t}\{W_r^{(s)}(h\,\Delta t) - W_r^{(s)}[(h-1)\,\Delta t]\}.$$

The coefficients 6, 30, 140, 630, etc., are the K_r in Eq. (3–34).

It may be noted that $W_1(n\,\Delta t) = 0$, so that there are only n terms in the smoothing sequence for first differences. This is to be expected because $n + 1$ data will yield only n first differences. For a similar reason $W_2(h\,\Delta t)$ is zero for $h = n - 1$, $h = n$, and so on for the other smoothing sequences.

These smoothing sequences may, of course, be regarded as variable smoothing sequences, by letting n increase by one for each Δt of real time. This is done in Chapter 9.

CHAPTER 8

DISCRETE SMOOTHING BY CASCADED SIMPLE AVERAGINGS

8.1 Cascaded simple weighting sequences. In the planning stages of some practical applications of discrete data smoothing and prediction, objections were raised against the weighting sequences or smoothing sequences formulated in Chapter 7, except $W_0(h\,\Delta t)$, on account of the large number of storage slots and arithmetical operations which they require for large values of $n = T/\Delta t$. At the same time, objections were raised against the recursive (that is, feedback type) discrete schemes described in Chapter 5 because the weighting sequences which they provide are infinitely long, and the weights beyond the prescribed smoothing time could not be made sufficiently small except by going to much higher orders of approximation.† These objections were avoided to a large extent by the schemes described in this chapter, as far at least as fixed (that is, time-invariant) schemes are concerned.

The schemes described here are based on the fact that, subject to some restrictions, a nonuniform weighting sequence of finite length may, in effect, be obtained by cascading simple (that is, uniform) weighting sequences of shorter lengths. (This idea is due to J. W. Tukey, *circa* 1950.) The effective weighting sequence is the multiple discrete convolution of the cascaded simple weighting sequences. For example, the convolution of the simple weighting sequence

$$\{7(1)\} = \{1, 1, 1, 1, 1, 1, 1\}$$

with the simple weighting sequence

$$\{4(1)\} = \{1, 1, 1, 1\}$$

is the weighting sequence

$$\{7(1)\} * \{4(1)\} = \{1, 2, 3, 4, 4, 4, 4, 3, 2, 1\}.$$

(The convolution of a sequence of m weights with a sequence of n weights is a sequence of $m + n - 1$ weights.) The convolution of this weighting sequence

---

† Equation (5–3) is equivalent to

$$v_k = \sum_{j=0}^{\infty} W_j u_{k-j}$$

where the W's are related to the A's and B's by

$$\frac{\sum_{\alpha=0}^{r} A_\alpha q^\alpha}{1 + \sum_{\beta=1}^{n} B_\beta q^\beta} = \sum_{j=0}^{\infty} W_j q^j.$$

with the simple weighting sequence

$$\{3(1)\} = \{1, 1, 1\}$$

is the weighting sequence

$$\{7(1)\} * \{4(1)\} * \{3(1)\} = \{1, 3, 6, 9, 11, 12, 12, 11, 9, 6, 3, 1\}.$$

This weighting sequence is shown in Fig. 8.1.

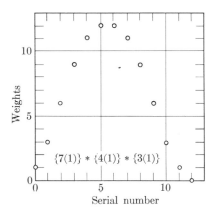

FIG. 8.1. Weights for an example of cascaded simple weighting sequences.

The advantage of cascaded simple averagings is obviously in the elimination of practically all of the multiplications. When differencing operations are combined with cascaded simple averagings, further simplification of the arithmetic may be achieved by combining each differencing operation with one of the simple averagings. For example, if

$$\{\Delta\} = \{1, -1\},$$

then

$$\{\Delta\} * \{7(1)\} = \{1, 0, 0, 0, 0, 0, 0, -1\}.$$

This corresponds to a single operation of differencing across seven intervals. Similarly,

$$\{\Delta\} * \{4(1)\} = \{1, 0, 0, 0, -1\}$$

corresponds to a single operation of differencing across four intervals. These two operations in cascade are equivalent to the weighting sequence

$$\{\Delta^2\} * \{7(1)\} * \{4(1)\} = \{1, 0, 0, 0, -1, 0, 0, -1, 0, 0, 0, 1\}$$

so that

$$\{\Delta^2\} * \{7(1)\} * \{4(1)\} * \{3(1)\} = \{1, 1, 1, 0, -1, -1, -1, -1, -1, -1, 0, 1, 1, 1\}.$$

The zeroth and first moments of this weighting sequence are, of course, zero.

In the following sections, we will derive the optimum relative lengths of the cascaded simple weighting sequences for smoothing differences of several orders under the assumption of bandlimited white noise, and we will compare the effectiveness of these schemes with those described in Chapter 7.

The weighting sequence $W_0(h\,\Delta t)$ described in Chapter 7 is already a simple averaging sequence. For the purposes of this chapter, it will be denoted by

$$w_0 = \frac{1}{n+1}\{n_1(1)\} \qquad (n_1 = n+1), \tag{8-1}$$

where $n_1(1)$ means n_1 consecutive ones.

8.2 Smoothed first differences. Consider the following procedure.

1.1 Keep the most recent $n_1 + 1$ terms of the original time series in store. (Here, n_1 is not as in Eq. 8–1.)

1.2 Generate each term of a second time series by taking the difference between the newest and the oldest terms stored in 1.1 and dividing by $n_1\,\Delta t$. Keep the most recent n_2 terms of this series in store ($n_2 \le n_1$).

1.3 Generate each term of the final output time series by summing the terms stored in 1.2 and dividing by n_2 (see top half of Fig. 8.2).

Clearly, the second time series represents moving simple averages of n_1 consecutive first differences. The whole scheme is equivalent to applying two

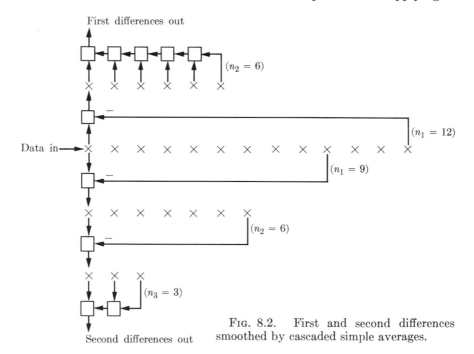

FIG. 8.2.   First and second differences smoothed by cascaded simple averages.

moving simple averagings, in cascade, to the first differences of the original time series.

Neglecting the divisions by $n_1 \Delta t$ and by n_2 for the moment, it may be seen that the scheme is equivalent to applying to the original time series a weighting sequence consisting of n_2 consecutive ones, followed by $(n_1 - n_2)$ consecutive zeros, and followed in turn by n_2 consecutive negative ones. Thus, the weighting sequence may be represented by

$$w_1 = \frac{1}{n_1 n_2 \, \Delta t} \{n_2(1), (n_1 - n_2)(0), n_2(-1)\}. \tag{8-2}$$

Hence, for bandlimited white noise of variance σ^2 and cutoff frequency $f_c = 1/(2 \, \Delta t)$, the variance of the noise in the output time series is

$$\bar{\sigma}^2_{1 \text{ sa}} = \frac{2n_2}{(n_1 n_2 \, \Delta t)^2} \sigma^2 \qquad (n_1 \geq n_2). \tag{8-3}$$

This is a minimum under the constraint $n_1 + n_2 = $ constant, when $n_1 = 2n_2$.

In order to compare the effectiveness of this scheme with that of the scheme using the weighting sequence $W_1^{(1)}(h \, \Delta t)$ of Chapter 7, we must take $n_1 + n_2 = n + 1$, so that

$$n_1 = \tfrac{2}{3}(n + 1), \qquad n_2 = \tfrac{1}{3}(n + 1). \tag{8-4}$$

Assuming $n + 1$ to be a multiple of 3, the weighting sequence is

$$w_1 = \frac{9}{2(n + 1)^2 \, \Delta t} \{n_2(1), n_2(0), n_2(-1)\}, \tag{8-5}$$

and the output/input noise variance ratio is

$$\frac{\bar{\sigma}^2_{1 \text{ sa}}}{\sigma^2} = \frac{27}{2(n + 1)^3 \, \Delta t^2}. \tag{8-6}$$

Comparing this result with the corresponding result in Chapter 7,

$$\frac{\bar{\sigma}^2_1}{\sigma^2} = \frac{12}{n(n + 1)(n + 2) \, \Delta t^2}, \tag{8-7}$$

we have

$$\frac{\bar{\sigma}^2_{1 \text{ sa}}}{\bar{\sigma}^2_1} = \frac{9}{8}\left[1 - \frac{1}{(n + 1)^2}\right] \approx 1.125.$$

The term "efficiency" is a standard statistical term for the reciprocal ratio $\bar{\sigma}^2_1/\bar{\sigma}^2_{1 \text{ sa}}$. The result $n_2 = (n + 1)/3$ was obtained by A. S. Eddington many years ago. (Eddington, who died in November, 1944, did not publish this result, but he is credited with it in Jeffreys, 1948, p. 193.) Eddington's interest was in estimating linear trend in recorded data, so that $n + 1$ represented all of the data. For data-smoothing in real time, n is flexible to some extent, so that it would be more appropriate to judge the effectiveness of the present scheme by the "recovery factor" η by which the smoothing time would have to be multiplied in order that $\bar{\sigma}_{1\,\text{sa}}^2 = \sigma_1^2$. Thus,

$$\eta \approx \left(\frac{9}{8}\right)^{1/3} \approx 1.040.$$

Equation (8–6) was derived under the assumption that $n + 1$ is a multiple of 3, and that n_1 and n_2 are taken in accordance with Eqs. (8–4). Suppose, however, that $n + 1 = 4$. Then, according to Eq. (8–3),

$$\frac{\bar{\sigma}_{1\,\text{sa}}^2}{\sigma^2} = \frac{1}{4\,\Delta t^2} \qquad \text{if } n_1 = 2, \quad n_2 = 2,$$

$$= \frac{2}{9\,\Delta t_2} \qquad \text{if } n_1 = 3, \quad n_2 = 1,$$

whereas Eq. (8–6), if it were applicable, gives $27/(128\,\Delta t^2)$. The optimum scheme according to Eq. (8–7) gives $1/(5\,\Delta t^2)$. Thus, the worse of the two alternatives ($n_1 = 2$ and $n_2 = 2$) gives an output variance which is only 25% higher than the output variance for the optimum scheme. This result shows that the choice of $n + 1$ as a multiple of 3 is not critical.

8.3 Smoothed second differences. For second differences, the procedure is as follows.

2.1 Keep the most recent $n_1 + 1$ terms of the original time series in store. (Here again, n_1 does not have the previous meanings.)

2.2 Generate each term of a second time series by taking the difference between the newest and the oldest terms stored in 2.1 and dividing by $n_1\,\Delta t$. Keep the most recent $n_2 + 1$ terms of this series in store ($n_2 \leq n_1$).

2.3 Generate each term of a third time series by taking the difference between the newest and the oldest terms stored in 2.2 and dividing by $n_2\,\Delta t$. Keep the most recent n_3 terms of this series in store ($n_3 \leq n_2$).

2.4 Generate each term of the final output time series by summing the terms stored in 2.3 and dividing by n_3 (see bottom half of Fig. 8.2).

This scheme is equivalent to applying three simple averagings, in cascade, to the second differences of the original time series.

In this case, it is very difficult to determine the optimum ratios of n_1, n_2, and n_3 to their sum $n_1 + n_2 + n_3 = n + 1$, using the same method as in the case of first differences. It is much less difficult to determine these optimum ratios by analyzing the corresponding continuous-time case in which, in effect, the second derivative is submitted to three simple continuous-time averagings of lengths T_1, T_2, and T_3, where $T_1 \geq T_2 \geq T_3 \geq 0$, and $T_1 + T_2 + T_3 = T$. (The essential details of this analysis are given in Appendix E.) It turns out that we should take

$$T_1 : T_2 : T_3 = 3 : 2 : 1.$$

Hence, in the discrete case, we take

$$n_1 = \tfrac{1}{2}(n+1), \quad n_2 = \tfrac{1}{3}(n+1), \quad n_3 = \tfrac{1}{6}(n+1). \tag{8-8}$$

Then, the scheme is equivalent to applying to the original time series, the weighting sequence

$$w_2 = \frac{36}{(n+1)^3 \, \Delta t^2} \, \{n_3(1), n_3(0), 2n_3(-1), n_3(0), n_3(1)\}. \tag{8-9}$$

For bandlimited white noise with cutoff frequency $f_c = 1/(2\,\Delta t)$, the output/input noise variance ratio is

$$\frac{\bar{\sigma}_{2\ \text{sa}}^2}{\sigma^2} = \frac{864}{(n+1)^5 \, \Delta t^4}. \tag{8-10}$$

Comparing this result with the corresponding result in Chapter 7, we have

$$\frac{\bar{\sigma}_{2\ \text{sa}}^2}{\bar{\sigma}_2^2} \approx 1.200, \qquad \text{and } \eta \approx (1.200)^{1/5} \approx 1.037.$$

Note that the output first and second differences in Fig. 8.2 are derived from the same block of 18 terms of the input data.

8.4 Smoothed third differences. For third differences, the procedure is as follows.

3.1 Keep the most recent $n_1 + 1$ terms of the original time series in store.

3.2 Generate each term of a second time series by taking the difference between the newest and the oldest terms stored in 3.1 and dividing by $n_1\,\Delta t$. Keep the most recent $n_2 + 1$ terms of this series in store $(n_2 \leq n_1)$.

3.3 Generate each term of a third time series by taking the difference between the newest and the oldest terms stored in 3.2 and dividing by $n_2\,\Delta t$. Keep the most recent $n_3 + 1$ terms of this series in store $(n_3 \leq n_2)$.

3.4 Generate each term of a fourth time series by taking the difference between the newest and the oldest terms stored in 3.3 and dividing by $n_3\,\Delta t$. Keep the most recent n_4 terms of this series in store $(n_4 \leq n_3)$.

3.5 Generate each term of the final output time series by summing the terms stored in 3.4 and dividing by n_4.

This scheme is equivalent to applying four simple averagings, in cascade, to the third differences of the original time series.

In this case, it is very difficult to determine the optimum ratios of n_1, n_2, n_3, and n_4 to their sum $n_1 + n_2 + n_3 + n_4 = n + 1$, even by analyzing the corresponding continuous-time case. It may be conjectured, however, that these numbers should be as $4:3:2:1$, so that

$$n_1 = \tfrac{2}{5}(n+1), \quad n_2 = \tfrac{3}{10}(n+1), \quad n_1 = \tfrac{1}{5}(n+1), \quad n_4 = \tfrac{1}{10}(n+1). \tag{8-11}$$

Then the scheme is equivalent to applying to the original time series the weighting sequence

$$w_3 = \frac{1250}{3(n+1)^4 \, \Delta t^3} \, \{n_4(1), \, n_4(0), \, 3n_4(-1), \, 3n_4(1), \, n_4(0), \, n_4(-1)\}. \qquad (8\text{--}12)$$

For bandlimited white noise with cutoff frequency $f_c = 1/(2 \, \Delta t)$, the output/input noise variance ratio is

$$\frac{\bar{\sigma}_{3 \, \text{sa}}^2}{\sigma^2} = \frac{10^7}{72(n+1)^7 \, \Delta t^6}. \qquad (8\text{--}13)$$

Comparing this result with the corresponding result in Chapter 7, we have

$$\frac{\bar{\sigma}_{3 \, \text{sa}}^2}{\bar{\sigma}_3^2} \approx 1.378, \qquad \text{and} \qquad \eta \approx (1.378)^{1/7} \approx 1.047.$$

If the conjectured optimum ratios of n_1, n_2, n_3, n_4, to $(n+1)$ are not exactly correct, they have the merit at least of being simple rational fractions. It would hardly be practical to attempt to conform to more refined theoretical results if the ratios turned out to be less simple, especially because the recovery factor is so close to one.

8.5 Smoothed fourth differences. Omitting the obvious details of the procedure for fourth differences, it may be conjectured that the lengths of the five simple averagings should be as $5:4:3:2:1$, so that

$$n_1 = \tfrac{1}{3}(n+1), \qquad n_2 = \tfrac{4}{15}(n+1), \qquad n_3 = \tfrac{1}{5}(n+1),$$
$$n_4 = \tfrac{2}{15}(n+1), \qquad n_5 = \tfrac{1}{15}(n+1). \qquad (8\text{--}14)$$

Then, the scheme is equivalent to applying to the original time series the weighting sequence

$$w_4 = \frac{(15)^4}{8(n+1)^5 \, \Delta t^4} \, \{n_5(1), \, n_5(0), \, 3n_5(-1), \, n_5(0), \, n_5(1),$$
$$n_5(2), \, n_5(1), \, n_5(0), \, 3n_5(-1), \, n_5(0), \, n_5(1)\}. \qquad (8\text{--}15)$$

For bandlimited white noise with cutoff frequency $f_c = 1/(2 \, \Delta t)$, the output/input noise variance ratio is

$$\frac{\bar{\sigma}_{4 \, \text{sa}}^2}{\sigma^2} = \frac{7 \, (15)^7}{32(n+1)^9 \, \Delta t^8}. \qquad (8\text{--}16)$$

Comparing this result with the corresponding result in Chapter 7, we have

$$\frac{\bar{\sigma}_{4 \, \text{sa}}^2}{\bar{\sigma}_4^2} \approx 1.471, \qquad \text{and} \qquad \eta \approx (1.471)^{1/9} \approx 1.044.$$

In the last three cases, as in the first, it is easily shown that the choice of $n + 1$ as a multiple of 6, or 10, or 15, as the case may be, is not critical.

8.6 Cross-correlation of noise outputs. Assuming a common source of band-limited white noise with cutoff frequency $f_c = 1/(2 \Delta t)$, the noise outputs of two schemes whose weighting sequences are $\alpha(h \Delta t)$ and $\beta(h \Delta t)$, respectively, will have a cross-correlation coefficient ρ, where

$$\rho = \frac{\sum_h [\alpha(h \Delta t) \beta(h \Delta t)]}{\sqrt{\sum_h [\alpha(h \Delta t)]^2 \sum_h [\beta(h \Delta t)]^2}}.$$

If $\alpha(h \Delta t)$ and $\beta(h \Delta t)$ are identified with $W_r^{(r)}(h \Delta t)$ and $W_s^{(s)}(h \Delta t)$, respectively, from Chapter 7, it will be found, of course, that the cross-correlation coefficient is zero if $r \neq s$.

If α and β are identified with a pair of weighting sequences from the set w_0, w_1, w_2, w_3, w_4 described in this chapter, it will be found that in eight out of the ten pairs the cross-correlation coefficient is zero. In each of the four pairs which involve w_0, the cross-correlation coefficient is zero because w_0 is a uniform weighting sequence and the other weighting sequence has a zeroth moment of zero. In each of the pairs (w_1, w_2), (w_1, w_4), (w_2, w_3), and (w_3, w_4), the cross-correlation coefficient is zero because one weighting sequence has even symmetry while the other weighting sequence has odd symmetry. The two pairs which give nonzero cross-correlation coefficients are

$$(w_1, w_3): \quad \rho = - \frac{1}{2\sqrt{30}} = -0.0913,$$

$$(w_2, w_4): \quad \rho = - \frac{3}{2\sqrt{35}} = -0.2535.$$

(Note that these are negative. Neglecting them in preliminary design studies will usually give somewhat pessimistic results.)

8.7 Moments of weighting sequences. The first six (zeroth to fifth) moments of the weighting sequence w_0 are:

$$M_0 = 1, \qquad M_1 = \frac{n}{2} \Delta t, \qquad M_2 = \frac{n(2n + 1)}{6} \Delta t^2,$$

$$M_3 = \frac{n^2(n + 1)}{4} \Delta t^3,$$

$$M_4 = \frac{n(2n + 1)(3n^2 + 3n - 1)}{30} \Delta t^4,$$

$$M_5 = \frac{n^2(n + 1)(2n^2 + 2n - 1)}{12} \Delta t^5.$$

Those of the weighting sequence w_1 are:

$$M_0 = 0, \quad M_1 = -1, \quad M_2 = -n\,\Delta t,$$

$$M_3 = -\frac{16n^2 + 5n - 2}{18}\,\Delta t^2,$$

$$M_4 = -\frac{n(n+1)(7n-2)}{9}\,\Delta t^3,$$

$$M_5 = -\frac{332n^4 + 383n^3 - 123n^2 - 67n + 26}{486}\,\Delta t^4.$$

Those of the weighting sequence w_2 are:

$$M_0 = M_1 = 0, \quad M_2 = 2, \quad M_3 = 3n\,\Delta t,$$

$$M_4 = \frac{61n^2 + 14n - 11}{18}\,\Delta t^2,$$

$$M_5 = \frac{5n(n+1)(25n-11)}{36}\,\Delta t^3.$$

Those of the weighting sequence w_3 are:

$$M_0 = M_1 = M_2 = 0, \quad M_3 = -6, \quad M_4 = -12n\,\Delta t,$$

$$M_5 = -\frac{33n^2 + 6n - 7}{2}\,\Delta t^2.$$

Those of the weighting sequence w_4 are:

$$M_0 = M_1 = M_2 = M_3 = 0, \quad M_4 = 24, \quad M_5 = 60n\,\Delta t.$$

8.8 General methods of computing variance ratios and moments. The formulas for variance ratios and moments given above, excepting those for w_0, are valid only if $n + 1$ is a multiple of 3 in the case of w_1, a multiple of 6 in the case of w_2, and so on. When it is expedient to abandon these restrictions, the variance ratios and moments may be determined from the actual weighting sequence which may be derived in two ways. For example, in the scheme for first differences, given n_1 and n_2, the weighting sequence may be derived by actually performing the discrete convolution

$$\frac{1}{n_1 n_2\,\Delta t}\,\{\Delta\} * \{n_1(1)\} * \{n_2(1)\}.$$

Alternatively, the weighting sequence may be derived by expanding the corresponding transfer function into a polynomial in q. The corresponding transfer function is clearly

$$\frac{1}{n_1 n_2\,\Delta t}\,(1-q)\,\frac{1-q^{n_1}}{1-q}\,\frac{1-q^{n_2}}{1-q},$$

or, after removing redundant factors, we have

$$\frac{1}{n_1 n_2 \,\Delta t} \frac{(1 - q^{n_1})(1 - q^{n_2})}{1 - q}.$$

8.9 Saving data storage slots. When the method of cascaded simple averages is used to obtain smoothed differences of more than one order from the same data, it is possible to arrange the computations so as to further reduce the required number of data storage slots. Consider the simple case in which first differences with $n_1 = 12$, $n_2 = 6$ and second differences with $n_1 = 9$, $n_2 = 6$, $n_3 = 3$ are desired. The arrangement shown in Fig. 8.2 requires 29 storage slots, but the arrangement shown in Fig. 8.3 requires only 22 storage slots (at the price of 5 more additions).

The arrangement in Fig. 8.3 was found by inspecting the transfer functions from an operational point of view. Taking $n + 1 = 6k$, which is divisible by both 3 and 6, the transfer functions expressed in forms which may be identified with the computational arrangement shown in Fig. 8.2 are

$$Y_1^{(1)} = \frac{1 - q^{2k}}{2k(1 - q)} \frac{1 - q^{4k}}{4k\,\Delta t} \qquad (k = 3),$$

$$Y_2^{(2)} = \frac{1 - q^{k}}{k(1 - q)} \frac{1 - q^{2k}}{2k\,\Delta t} \frac{1 - q^{3k}}{3k\,\Delta t},$$

where, from the operational point of view, $(1 - q^{\alpha})/\alpha\,\Delta t$ means "take divided differences across α intervals," and $(1 - q^{\beta})/\beta(1 - q)$ means "take simple

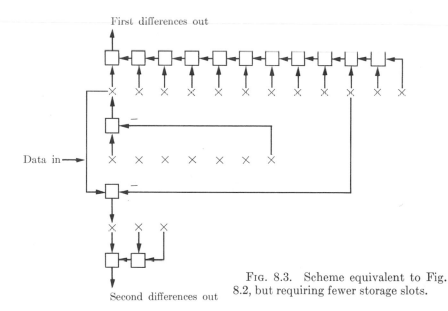

First differences out

Data in→

Second differences out

FIG. 8.3. Scheme equivalent to Fig. 8.2, but requiring fewer storage slots.

averages over β points." However, these transfer functions may also be expressed in the forms

$$Y_1^{(1)} = \frac{1 - q^{4k}}{4k(1 - q)} \frac{1 - q^{2k}}{2k \, \Delta t},$$

$$Y_2^{(2)} = \frac{1 - q^k}{k(1 - q)} \frac{1 - q^{3k}}{3k \, \Delta t} \frac{1 - q^{2k}}{2k \, \Delta t}.$$

These forms may be identified with the computational arrangement shown in Fig. 8.3.

The following table taken from Blackman (1960) is a comparison of the requirements of four nonrecursive schemes for deriving a smoothed and predicted (or updated) first difference and the smoothed second difference in a case in which $n + 1 = 168$.

| | Optimum | | CSA | Modified CSA |
	Direct	Step-by-Step		
Data slots	335	335	254	197
Slots for multipliers	250	168	6	5
Total slots	585	503	260	202
Multiplications	250	168	6	5
Additions	337	338	90	144

In the direct and step-by-step optimum methods, we require 2 slots for input data, 167 for raw first differences, and 166 for raw second differences. In the direct optimum method, the smoothed and predicted (or updated) first difference is obtained by applying to the 167 raw first differences the weighting sequence

$$W_1(h \, \Delta t) + kW_2^{(1)}(h \, \Delta t),$$

in the notation of Chapter 7 so that

$$W_2^{(1)}(h \, \Delta t) = \frac{1}{\Delta t} \{W_2(h \, \Delta t) - W_2[(h - 1) \, \Delta t]\}$$

$$= \frac{60}{\Delta t} \frac{(1 + h)(n - 1 - 2h)(n - h)}{(n - 1)n(n + 1)(n + 2)(n + 3)}.$$

This weighting sequence is the discrete version of the weighting function $W_1(\tau) + kW_2^{(1)}(\tau)$ in the notation of Figs. 2.2 and 2.3. It is asymmetrical. On the other hand, the weighting sequence $W_2(h \, \Delta t)$ applied to the 166 raw second differences is symmetrical. Hence, we need $167 + 83 = 250$ slots for multipliers. For a smoothed and updated first difference, as well as for a smoothed and predicted first difference, we need 167 more slots for multipliers.

In the step-by-step optimum method (discrete version of Figs. 2.2 and 2.3, of which the advantages over the direct method were noted in Chapter 2) the smoothed first difference, without prediction or delay-correction, is obtained by applying the symmetrical weighting sequence $W_1(h \, \Delta t)$ to the 167 raw first differences. Hence, we need $84 + 83 + 1 = 168$ slots for multipliers, including one for the k-factor for prediction (or updating) of the smoothed first difference. For a smoothed and updated first difference, as well as a smoothed and predicted first difference, we need only one more slot for another k-factor.

The numbers tabulated for CSA (cascaded simple averages) and for Modified CSA are based on the configurations shown in Figs. 8.2 and 8.3, respectively.

For another way of rearranging the computations, see O'Donohue (1962).

8.10 Estimation of satellite orbital parameters.   In this section we will describe a scheme for computing estimates of the orbital parameters of an artificial satellite from recorded radar tracking data. This scheme may also be regarded as the last stage of a more complicated scheme which has generated range data from "angles only" tracking data. It does not operate in real time. It cannot be put into operation until all of the single-pass data to be processed have been recorded.

In order to simplify this description we will assume that the only force acting on the satellite is directed towards the centroid of the earth and is inversely proportional to the square of the geocentric distance. Thus, the orbit is strictly a fixed ellipse or circle in an inertial plane. We will assume also that, except for random tracking errors, the data represent the actual position of the satellite relative to the tracker at uniform intervals Δt of time extending over a total of $2k$ points during one pass of the satellite through the observational zone of the tracker. Thus, no consideration is given to the refraction or the finite velocity of propagation of electromagnetic waves.

A flow diagram of the scheme is shown in Fig. 8.4 in which most of the notation is as follows.

D, E, A: range, elevation angle, and azimuth (standard radar tracking coordinates).

i: subscript running from 1 to $2k$ referring any quantity to time t_i.

x, y, z: rectangular coordinates referred to the usual geocentric inertial axes, with z along the earth's spin axis, and x toward the vernal equinox.

Ω, I: longitude of ascending node, and inclination of orbital plane.

r, θ: geocentric distance, and geocentric angle from ascending node in the orbital plane.

$r_c, \dot{r}_c, \theta_c, \dot{\theta}_c$: estimates of $r, \dot{r}, \theta, \dot{\theta}$ at time $t_c = (1/2k)\sum t_i$. These estimates are gradually improved by an iteration procedure.

$\hat{r}, \hat{\theta}$: values of r, θ, computed for a Keplerian orbit assuming the estimates $r_c, \dot{r}_c, \theta_c, \dot{\theta}_c$ are correct.

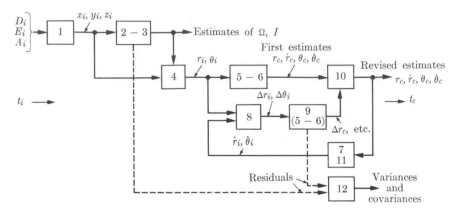

FIG. 8.4. Scheme for estimation of satellite orbital parameters.

The meaning of the other symbols in Fig. 8.4 will become clear from the following rough description of the computational steps which are numbered in accordance with the boxes in the diagram.

Step 1: coordinate conversion.

Step 2: computation of $\tilde{\Omega}_j$'s and $\tilde{I}_j$'s, where j runs from 1 to k.

Let $\mathbf{r}_i$ be the vector whose components are x_i, y_i, z_i. Then the vector-product $\mathbf{r}_j \times \mathbf{r}_{j+k}$, where j runs from 1 to k, is perpendicular to the plane of the two vectors. The estimate $\tilde{\Omega}_j$ of Ω is determined by the x- and y-components of the vector-product. The estimate $\tilde{I}_j$ of I is determined by the resultant of the x- and y-components and of the z-component. For greater accuracy the vector-product should be defined as $(\mathbf{r}_j + \mathbf{r}_{j+k}) \times (\mathbf{r}_{j+k} - \mathbf{r}_j)$.

Step 3: computation of averages $\Omega = (1/k)\sum\tilde{\Omega}_j$, and $I = (1/k)\sum\tilde{I}_j$, and of residuals $\Delta\tilde{\Omega}_j = \tilde{\Omega}_j - \Omega$, and $\Delta\tilde{I}_j = \tilde{I}_j - I$.

Step 4: computation of r_i's and θ_i's.

Step 5: computation of $\tilde{r}_j$'s, $\tilde{\dot{r}}_j$'s, $\tilde{\theta}_j$'s, and $\tilde{\dot{\theta}}_j$'s, where j runs from 1 to k.

$$\tilde{r}_j = \tfrac{1}{2}(r_j + r_{j+k}), \qquad \tilde{\dot{r}}_j = \frac{1}{k\,\Delta t}(r_{j+k} - r_j),$$

$$\tilde{\theta}_j = \tfrac{1}{2}(\theta_j + \theta_{j+k}), \qquad \tilde{\dot{\theta}}_j = \frac{1}{k\,\Delta t}(\theta_{j+k} - \theta_j).$$

Step 6: computation of averages

$$r_c = (1/k)\sum\tilde{r}_j, \qquad \dot{r}_c = (1/k)\sum\tilde{\dot{r}}_j,$$

$$\theta_c = (1/k)\sum\tilde{\theta}_j, \qquad \dot{\theta}_c = (1/k)\sum\tilde{\dot{\theta}}_j.$$

Step 7: computation of $\hat{r}_j$'s and $\hat{\theta}_i$'s (previously defined). *Note:* Steps 5 and 6 may be omitted if initial estimates of r_c, $\dot{r}_c$, θ_c, and $\dot{\theta}_c$ are available, as would usually be the case.

Step 8: computation of "residuals" $\Delta r_i = r_i - \hat{r}_i$, and $\Delta \theta_i = \theta_i - \hat{\theta}_i$.

Step 9: computation of corrections Δr_c, $\Delta \dot{r}_c$, $\Delta \theta_c$, and $\Delta \dot{\theta}_c$ from the "residuals" Δr_i's and $\Delta \theta_i$'s. Except for the nature of the quantities involved, this step is the same as Steps 5 and 6 in the computation of r_c, $\dot{r}_c$, θ_c, and $\dot{\theta}_c$ from the r_i's and θ_i's.

Step 10: revision of estimates r_c, $\dot{r}_c$, θ_c, $\dot{\theta}_c$ by addition of Δr_c, $\Delta \dot{r}_c$, $\Delta \theta_c$, and $\Delta \dot{\theta}_c$.

Step 11: reiteration of Steps 7–10 until corrections in Step 9 are negligible. Steps 7–10 constitute the "trend removal" cycle. At the end, the $\Delta \tilde{r}_j$'s, $\Delta \tilde{\dot{r}}_j$'s, $\Delta \tilde{\theta}_j$'s, and $\Delta \tilde{\dot{\theta}}_j$'s, which were not explicitly mentioned in the description of Step 9 but which are analogous to the $\tilde{r}_j$'s, $\tilde{\dot{r}}_j$'s, $\tilde{\theta}_j$'s, and $\tilde{\dot{\theta}}_j$'s computed in Step 5, are (trend-free) residuals in the same sense as the $\Delta \tilde{\Omega}_j$'s and $\Delta \tilde{I}_j$'s computed in Step 3.

Step 12: computation of 6 variances and 15 covariances from the 6 sets of residuals.

The covariance matrix obtained in the last step is a measure of the joint probability distribution of the errors in the estimates of the orbital parameters Ω, I, r_c, $\dot{r}_c$, θ_c, and $\dot{\theta}_c$. It is useful in the "combination of estimates" obtained from separate passes of the satellite over the same tracker or over separate trackers.

The method of combining estimates from separate passes, in its most direct and general form, may be stated briefly as follows. If x_1 and x_2 are independent estimates of a vector quantity x (where the term "vector" is used in the algebraic sense, conventionally represented by a one-column matrix), and if C_1 and C_2 are the corresponding covariance matrices, then the best combination of the estimates is

$$\bar{x} = (C_1^{-1} + C_2^{-1})^{-1}(C_1^{-1}x_1 + C_2^{-1}x_2),$$

with covariance matrix

$$\bar{C} = (C_1^{-1} + C_2^{-1})^{-1}.$$

The formula for $\bar{x}$ minimizes the quadratic form

$$Q = (x_1 - \bar{x})'C_1^{-1}(x_1 - \bar{x}) + (x_2 - \bar{x})'C_2^{-1}(x_2 - \bar{x}),$$

which may be rewritten in the form

$$Q = [\bar{x} - \bar{C}(C_1^{-1}x_1 + C_2^{-1}x_2)]'\bar{C}^{-1}[\bar{x} - \bar{C}(C_1^{-1}x_1 + C_2^{-1}x_2)] +$$

terms independent of $\bar{x}$.

This method of combining estimates from separate passes of the satellite is a way of avoiding the necessity of processing simultaneously all of the observational data from two or more passes. The number of points per pass typically runs to about 100 or more, depending upon the total tracking time.

The method of combining estimates from separate passes described above was used with a method of obtaining single-pass estimates from angles-only data in the Telstar I experiments (Claus, Blackman, Halline, and Ridgway, 1963). This method and some other methods of orbit refinement are discussed in Blackman, 1964.

CHAPTER 9

VARIABLE SMOOTHING SCHEMES

9.1 A situation for variable smoothing. Consider the following situation for the application of data smoothing schemes.

(a) The character of the signal, and perhaps also that of the noise, changes abruptly and so radically at some determinate time, say t_0, that it would be inimical to allow any of the data received before t_0 to influence subsequent computations.

(b) The results of the subsequent computations will determine (and perhaps will be used to determine some action at) a critical time t_c which has some such probability density distribution as that shown in Fig. 9.1, where $\Delta t_{\max}$ exceeds the optimum smoothing time.

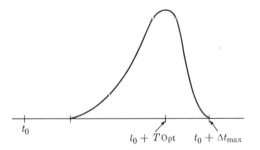

FIG. 9.1. Hypothetical probability density
distribution of critical time t_c.

(c) Conditions at t_0 are not determinate to a sufficient accuracy to permit the use of "preloading" as a method of effectively reducing the settling time of fixed smoothing schemes.

Since a fixed smoothing scheme without preloading has a settling time which is at least as long as its smoothing time, it is clear that the situation described above calls for variable smoothing schemes in which the weighting function $W(\tau;t)$ extends over $0 \leq \tau \leq t - t_0$, no more and preferably no less.

Except for an introductory general discussion of variable smoothing schemes in Chapter 1 and a casual reference to them at the end of Chapter 7, we have not considered such schemes from a practical point of view. In this chapter we will describe some of the ways in which variable smoothing schemes have been considered for practical use.

9.2 Variable continuous schemes. The particular schemes described in this section are based on the weighting functions denoted by $W_r(\tau)$ in Chapter 4 but are now rewritten for variable smoothing as

$$W_r(\tau;t) = \frac{K_r}{t}\left[\frac{\tau}{t}\left(1 - \frac{\tau}{t}\right)\right]^r \qquad \text{for } 0 \leq \tau \leq t,$$

$$= 0 \qquad \text{otherwise.}$$

The differential equation relating the response $V(t)$ to the excitation $E(t)$ will be derived from the requirement that its particular solution should be

$$V(t) = \int_0^t W_r(t - \lambda;t)E(\lambda)\, d\lambda \qquad \text{for } t > 0.$$

The circuits will then be designed from the differential equation.

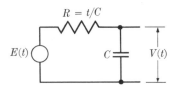

FIG. 9.2. Scheme for rectangular weighting function of increasing length but constant area.

For $W_0(\tau;t)$ we have

$$V(t) = \frac{1}{t}\int_0^t E(\lambda)\, d\lambda.$$

Multiplying through by t, and differentiating with respect to t, we get

$$t\frac{dV}{dt} + V = E.$$

This differential equation may be realized with a scheme of the form shown in Fig. 9.2, which is a special case of Fig. 1.2. For $0 < t < a$, it may also be realized with a more practical scheme of the form shown in Fig. 9.3 (due to S. Darlington).

For $W_1(\tau;t)$ we have

$$V(t) = \frac{6}{t^3}\int_0^t \lambda(t - \lambda)E(\lambda)\, d\lambda.$$

Multiplying through by $t^3/6$, differentiating twice with respect to t, and dividing through by t, we get

$$\frac{t^2}{6}\frac{d^2V}{dt^2} + t\frac{dV}{dt} + V = E.$$

This differential equation may be expressed in the factored operational form (first noted by B. T. Weber)

$$\left(\frac{t}{2}\frac{d}{dt} + 1\right)\left(\frac{t}{3}\frac{d}{dt} + 1\right)V = E.$$

For $0 < t < a$, this differential equation may be realized with a cascade (or tandem combination) of two schemes of the form shown in Fig. 9.4, with $k = 2$ for one scheme and $k = 3$ for the other scheme.

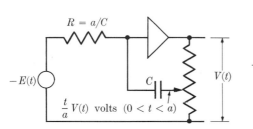

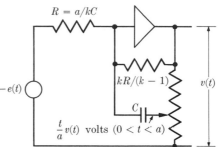

FIG. 9.3. A more practical realization of the scheme of Fig. 9.2.

FIG. 9.4.   Generalization of the scheme of Fig. 9.3.

For $W_2(\tau;t)$ we have

$$V(t) = \frac{30}{t^5} \int_0^t [\lambda(t - \lambda)]^2 E(\lambda) \, d\lambda.$$

Multiplying through by $t^5/60$, differentiating three times with respect to t, and dividing through by t^2, we get

$$\frac{t^3}{60} \frac{d^3V}{dt^3} + \frac{t^2}{4} \frac{d^2V}{dt^2} + t \frac{dV}{dt} + V = E.$$

This differential equation may be expressed in the factored operational form

$$\left(\frac{t}{3} \frac{d}{dt} + 1\right)\left(\frac{t}{4} \frac{d}{dt} + 1\right)\left(\frac{t}{5} \frac{d}{dt} + 1\right) V - E.$$

For $0 < t < a$, it may be realized with a cascade of three schemes of the form shown in Fig. 9.4.

9.3 Stopped variable continuous schemes. The differential equation for the scheme shown in Fig. 9.3 is

$$t \frac{dV}{dt} + V = E \qquad \text{for } 0 < t < a,$$

$$a \frac{dV}{dt} = E \qquad \text{for } t > a.$$

Hence

$$V(t) = \int_0^t W(t - \lambda;t) E(\lambda) \, d\lambda \qquad (t > 0),$$

where the following relations hold:

$$W(\tau;t) = \frac{1}{t} \quad \begin{cases} \text{for } 0 < t < a, \\ \text{and } 0 < \tau < t, \end{cases}$$

$$= \frac{1}{a} \quad \begin{cases} \text{for } t > a, \\ \text{and } 0 < \tau < t. \end{cases}$$

For the scheme shown in Fig. 9.4, we have

$$W(\tau;t) = \frac{k}{t^k}(t - \tau)^{k-1} \quad \begin{cases} \text{for } 0 < t < a, \\ \text{and } 0 < \tau < t, \end{cases}$$

$$= \frac{k}{a}e^{-[(k-1)/a]\tau} \quad \begin{cases} \text{for } t > a, \\ \text{and } 0 < \tau < t - a, \end{cases}$$

$$= \frac{k}{a^k}e^{-[(k-1)/a](t-a)}(t - \tau)^{k-1} \quad \begin{cases} \text{for } t > a, \\ \text{and } t - a < \tau < t. \end{cases}$$

Since, in either case,

$$\int_0^t W(\tau;t)\, d\tau = 1 \qquad\qquad\qquad \text{for } 0 < t < a,$$

$$= 1 + \frac{1}{k-1}\left[1 - e^{-[(k-1)/a](t-a)}\right] \quad \text{for } t > a,$$

these schemes cannot be used for $t > a$ without some modification.

Now, consider the scheme shown in Fig. 9.5. The differential equation relating the response $V(t)$ to the excitation $E(t)$ is

$$\frac{\varphi(t)}{k\dot{\varphi}(t)}\frac{dV}{dt} + V = E,$$

as long as $0 \le F_C(t) \le 1$ and $0 \le F_R(t) \le 1$. The particular solution is

$$V(t) = \int_0^t W(t - \lambda;t)E(\lambda)\, d\lambda \qquad (t > 0),$$

where

$$W(\tau;t) = -\frac{\partial}{\partial\tau}\left[\frac{\varphi(t - \tau)}{\varphi(t)}\right]^k \qquad (0 < \tau < t).$$

Since

$$\int_0^t W(\tau;t)\, d\tau = 1 - \left[\frac{\varphi(0)}{\varphi(t)}\right]^k,$$

the scheme may be used for all $t > 0$ provided that $\varphi(0) = 0$, and $\varphi(t)$ is other-

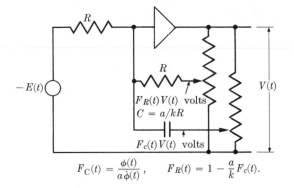

$$F_C(t) = \frac{\phi(t)}{a\,\dot\phi(t)}, \qquad F_R(t) = 1 - \frac{a}{k}F_c(t).$$

FIG. 9.5. A scheme which is variable for $0 < t < a$, but fixed for $t > a$.

wise suitably chosen so that $0 \le F_C(t) \le 1$ and $0 \le F_R(t) \le 1$ for all $t > 0$. As an example, let

$$\varphi(t) = \frac{t}{a} \qquad \text{for } 0 < t < a,$$

$$= e^{(t-a)/a} \qquad \text{for } t > a.$$

Then

$$F_C(t) = \frac{t}{a} \qquad \text{for } 0 < t < a,$$

$$= 1 \qquad \text{for } t > a,$$

and

$$F_R(t) = 1 - \frac{1}{k} \qquad \text{for } 0 < t < a,$$

$$= 1 \qquad \text{for } t > a.$$

In this example, the F_R potentiometer is superfluous. The feedback resistance needs only to be switched from a value of $kR/(k-1)$ for $0 < t < a$ to a value of R for $t > a$. (If $k = 1$, this simply means that the resistor is switched out while $t < a$.) The weighting function in this example is

$$W(\tau;t) = \frac{k}{t^k}(t-\tau)^{k-1} \qquad \begin{array}{l} \text{for } 0 < t < a, \\ \text{and } 0 < \tau < t, \end{array}$$

$$= \frac{k}{a}e^{-(k/a)\tau} \qquad \begin{array}{l} \text{for } t > a, \\ \text{and } 0 < \tau < t - a, \end{array}$$

$$= \frac{k}{a^k}e^{-(k/a)(t-a)}(t-\tau)^{k-1} \qquad \begin{array}{l} \text{for } t > a, \\ \text{and } t - a < \tau < t. \end{array}$$

This weighting function is plotted in Fig. 9.6 as a function of τ, for $k = 1$, $a = 10$, and $t = 2, 5, 10, 17$, remembering that it is zero for $\tau > t$ as well as for $\tau < 0$.

As a second example, let

$$\varphi(t) = \left(\frac{t}{2a - t}\right)^{1/2} \qquad \text{for } 0 < t < a,$$

$$= e^{(t-a)/a} \qquad \text{for } t > a.$$

Then

$$F_C(t) = \frac{t(2a - t)}{a^2} \qquad \text{for } 0 < t < a,$$

$$= 1 \qquad \text{for } t > a,$$

and, if $k = 2$,

$$F_R(t) = \frac{t}{a} \qquad \text{for } 0 < t < a,$$

$$= 1 \qquad \text{for } t > a.$$

The weighting function in this example is

$$W(\tau;t) = \frac{2a(2a - t)}{t(2a - t + \tau)^2} \qquad \begin{array}{l} \text{for } 0 < t < a, \\ \text{and } 0 < \tau < t, \end{array}$$

$$= \frac{2}{a} e^{-(2/a)\tau} \qquad \begin{array}{l} \text{for } t > a, \\ \text{and } 0 < \tau < t - a, \end{array}$$

$$= \frac{2ae^{-(2/a)(t-a)}}{(2a - t + \tau)^2} \qquad \begin{array}{l} \text{for } t > a, \\ \text{and } t - a < \tau < t. \end{array}$$

The differential equation for the scheme shown in Fig. 9.5 was derived from the equation

$$C\frac{d}{dt}(F_C V) + \frac{F_R}{R} V - \frac{E}{R} = 0.$$

Now, let us assume that the condenser C is charged to the full voltage $V(t)$ at all times and that it is practicable to feed back only the fraction $\hat{F}_C(t)$ of the

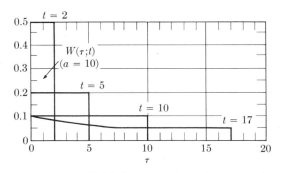

FIG. 9.6.   Weighting function of a typical stopped variable scheme.

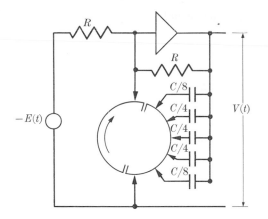

FIG. 9.7. A Darlington stopped variable scheme.

current through the condenser. Then, with $\hat{F}_R(t)$ in place of $F_R(t)$, we have

$$C\hat{F}_C \frac{dV}{dt} + \frac{\hat{F}_R}{R} V - \frac{E}{R} = 0.$$

These differential equations are equivalent if

$$\hat{F}_C(t) = F_C(t), \qquad \hat{F}_R(t) = F_R(t) + RC \frac{d}{dt} F_C(t).$$

Hence, for the first example of the scheme, $\hat{F}_R(t) = 1$ for $0 < t < a$ as well as for $t > a$. Not only is the $\hat{F}_R$ potentiometer superfluous, but there is also no need to switch the feedback resistance. This idea is implicit to the scheme shown in Fig. 9.7 (due essentially to S. Darlington) which is approximately equivalent to the first example of the scheme shown in Fig. 9.5. All of the condensers in Fig. 9.7 are always charged to the same potential, $V(t)$, but they are introduced into the feedback loop one by one as the commutator rotates through half a revolution. Let there be $n + 1$ condensers of total capacity C, the first and the last having a capacity of $C/(2n)$ each and the other $n - 1$ having a capacity of C/n. The first condenser is switched into feedback at $t = 0$, the rth condenser $(r = 2, 3, \ldots, n)$ at $t = (r - 1) \Delta t$, where

$$\Delta t = \frac{RC}{n},$$

and the last condenser at $t = n \Delta t$. Then the differential equation relating the response $V(t)$ to the excitation $E(t)$ is

$$F(t) \frac{dV}{dt} + V = E,$$

where the following relations hold:

$$F(\xi) = \frac{\Delta t}{2} \qquad\qquad 0 < \xi < \Delta t,$$

$$= \frac{3\,\Delta t}{2} \qquad\qquad \Delta t < \xi < 2\,\Delta t,$$

$$= \frac{5\,\Delta t}{2} \qquad\qquad 2\,\Delta t < \xi < 3\,\Delta t,$$

$$\vdots \qquad\qquad\qquad \vdots$$

$$= (n - \tfrac{1}{2})\,\Delta t \qquad (n-1)\,\Delta t < \xi < n\,\Delta t,$$

$$= n\,\Delta t \qquad\qquad \xi > n\,\Delta t.$$

The particular solution is

$$V(t) = e^{-G(t)} \int_0^t \frac{e^{G(\lambda)}}{F(\lambda)}\, E(\lambda)\, d\lambda,$$

where

$$G(\lambda) = \int_0^\lambda \frac{d\xi}{F(\xi)}$$

$$= \frac{2\lambda}{\Delta t} \qquad\qquad 0 < \lambda < \Delta t,$$

$$= \frac{2(2\,\Delta t + \lambda)}{3\,\Delta t} \qquad \Delta t < \lambda < 2\,\Delta t,$$

$$= \frac{2(14\,\Delta t + 3\lambda)}{15\,\Delta t} \qquad 2\,\Delta t < \lambda < 3\,\Delta t,$$

and so on. The weighting function is

$$W(\tau;t) = e^{-G(t)} \frac{e^{G(t-\tau)}}{F(t-\tau)},$$

$$= -e^{-G(t)} \frac{\partial}{\partial \tau}\, e^{G(t-\tau)} \qquad (0 < \tau < t).$$

The area of the weighting function is

$$\int_0^t W(\tau;t)\, d\tau = 1 - e^{-G(t)} \qquad (t > 0).$$

Obviously this is also the response for $t > 0$, due to a unit step excitation applied at $t \le 0$. This step response (settling characteristic) approaches unity faster than the step response of the corresponding fixed scheme in which the total capacity C is in the feedback loop from the start.

9.4 A variable continuous scheme assuming a special type of nonstationary noise. A variable continuous scheme for velocity estimation has been derived by Burford (1958) assuming a special but not unusual type of nonstationary noise which is the product of a stationary noise and a deterministic function of time.

9.5 Variable discrete schemes. The particular schemes described in this section are based on the weighting sequences denoted by $W_r(h \, \Delta t)$ in Chapter 7 but are now adapted for variable discrete smoothing by letting n increase by one for each Δt of real time. For convenience, however, we will use a different notation here.

In analogy to the convolution formula in continuous time,

$$v(t) = \int_0^t W(\tau;t) u(t - \tau) \, d\tau \qquad (t \geq 0),$$

we write the convolution formula in discrete time in the form

$$v_n = \sum_{r=0}^{n} W_{rn} u_{n-r} \qquad (n = 0, 1, 2, \ldots).$$

The weighting coefficients will depend, as in Chapter 7, upon whether

$$u_k = x_k,$$

or

$$u_k = \frac{\Delta x_k}{\Delta t} = \frac{x_k - x_{k-1}}{\Delta t},$$

or

$$u_k = \frac{\Delta^2 x_k}{\Delta t^2} = \frac{x_k - 2x_{k-1} + x_{k-2}}{\Delta t^2},$$

or higher order divided differences of the original time series $\{x_k\}$.

For the case in which $u_k = x_k$, we should take

$$W_{rn} = \frac{1}{n + 1}.$$

Then,

$$(n + 1)v_n = \sum_{r=0}^{n} u_{n-r} = \sum_{s=0}^{n} u_s.$$

Substituting $n - 1$ for n, we get

$$nv_{n-1} = \sum_{s=0}^{n-1} u_s.$$

Subtracting the last equation from the preceding equation, we get

$$(n + 1)v_n - nv_{n-1} = u_n.$$

The most convenient form for actual computation is probably

$$v_n = v_{n-1} + \frac{1}{n+1}(u_n - v_{n-1}). \tag{9-1}$$

For later reference, however, we should note the operational form

$$(n\Delta + 1)v_n = u_n, \tag{9-2}$$

where

$$\Delta v_n = v_n - v_{n-1}.$$

For the case in which $u_k = \Delta x_k/\Delta t$, we should take

$$W_{rn} = 6\frac{(1+r)(n-r)}{n(n+1)(n+2)}.$$

(Note that while r formally goes up to n, actually $W_{nn} = 0$. This is consistent with the fact that $n+1$ values will yield only n first differences.) Then,

$$n(n+1)(n+2)v_n = 6\sum_{s=1}^{n} s(n+1-s)u_s.$$

Substituting $n - 1$ for n, we get

$$(n-1)n(n+1)v_{n-1} = 6\sum_{s=1}^{n-1} s(n-s)u_s.$$

Substituting $(n-1)$ for n once more, we get

$$(n-2)(n-1)nv_{n-2} = 6\sum_{s=1}^{n-2} s(n-1-s)u_s.$$

Multiplying these three equations by 1, -2, 1, respectively, adding, and dividing through by n, we get

$$(n+1)(n+2)v_n - 2(n-1)(n+1)v_{n-1} + (n-1)(n-2)v_{n-2} = 6u_n.$$

The most convenient form for actual computation, in a single equation, is probably

$$v_n = v_{n-1} + \frac{6}{(n+1)(n+2)}(u_n - v_{n-1}) + \frac{(n-1)(n-2)}{(n+1)(n+2)}(v_{n-1} - v_{n-2}). \tag{9-3}$$

However, this equation may be replaced by two cascaded equations of simpler form. The operational form of either of the last two equations is

$$\left\{\frac{(n-1)(n-2)}{6}\Delta^2 + (n-1)\Delta + 1\right\}v_n = u_n,$$

where $\Delta^2 v_n = v_n - 2v_{n-1} + v_{n-2}$. This may be rewritten in the factored form

$$\left\{\frac{n-1}{2}\Delta + 1\right\}\left\{\frac{n-1}{3}\Delta + 1\right\}v_n = u_n$$

because

$$\Delta[(n-1)\Delta v_n] = (n-1)\Delta v_n - (n-2)\Delta v_{n-1}$$

$$= (n-2)\Delta^2 v_n + \Delta v_n.$$

Then,

$$\left\{\frac{n-1}{2}\Delta + 1\right\}\alpha_n = u_n,$$

if

$$\left\{\frac{n-1}{3}\Delta + 1\right\}v_n = \alpha_n,$$

so that Eq. (9–3) may be replaced by the pair of cascaded equations

$$\alpha_n = \alpha_{n-1} + \frac{2}{n+1}(u_n - \alpha_{n-1}),$$

$$v_n = v_{n-1} + \frac{3}{n+2}(\alpha_n - v_{n-1}). \tag{9–4}$$

For the case in which $u_k = \Delta^2 x_k/\Delta t^2$, we should take

$$W_{rn} = 30\frac{(1+r)(2+r)(n-1-r)(n-r)}{(n-1)n(n+1)(n+2)(n+3)}.$$

(The fact that W_{nn} and $W_{(n-1)n}$ are zero is consistent with the fact that $n+1$ values will yield only $n-1$ second differences.) Then

$$(n-1)n(n+1)(n+2)(n+3)v_n = 30\sum_{s=2}^{n}s(s-1)(n+2-s)(n+1-s)u_s.$$

Substituting $n-1$ for n three times in succession, multiplying the four equations by 1, -3, 3, -1 respectively, adding, and dividing by $n(n-1)$, we get

$$(n+1)(n+2)(n+3)v_n - 3(n-2)(n+1)(n+2)v_{n-1}$$
$$+ 3(n-3)(n-2)(n+1)v_{n-2} - (n-2)(n-3)(n-4)v_{n-3} = 60u_n.$$

The most convenient form for actual computation in a single equation is probably

$$v_n = v_{n-1} + \frac{60}{(n+1)(n+2)(n+3)}(u_n - v_{n-1})$$

$$+ \frac{3(n-2)(n-3)}{(n+2)(n+3)}(v_{n-1} - v_{n-2})$$

$$+ \frac{(n-2)(n-3)(n-4)}{(n+1)(n+2)(n+3)}(v_{n-3} - v_{n-1}). \tag{9–5}$$

However, this equation may be replaced by three cascaded equations of simpler form. The operational form of either of the last two equations is

$$\left\{\frac{(n-2)(n-3)(n-4)}{60}\Delta^3 + \frac{(n-2)(n-3)}{4}\Delta^2 + (n-2)\Delta + 1\right\}v_n = u_n,$$

where $\Delta^3 v_n = v_n - 3v_{n-1} + 3v_{n-2} - v_{n-3}$. This may be rewritten in the factored form

$$\left\{\frac{n-2}{3}\Delta + 1\right\}\left\{\frac{n-2}{4}\Delta + 1\right\}\left\{\frac{n-2}{5}\Delta + 1\right\}v_n = u_n$$

because

$$\Delta[(n-2)\Delta v_n] = (n-2)\Delta v_n - (n-3)\Delta v_{n-1}$$
$$= (n-3)\Delta^2 v_n + \Delta v_n,$$

and

$$\Delta\{(n-2)\Delta[(n-2)\Delta v_n]\} = (n-2)[(n-3)\Delta^2 v_n + \Delta v_n]$$
$$- (n-3)[(n-4)\Delta^2 v_{n-1} + \Delta v_{n-1}]$$
$$= (n-3)(n-4)\Delta^3 v_n + 3(n-3)\Delta^2 v_n + \Delta v_n.$$

Then,

$$\left\{\frac{n-2}{3}\Delta + 1\right\}\alpha_n = u_n,$$

if

$$\left\{\frac{n-2}{4}\Delta + 1\right\}\beta_n = \alpha_n,$$

and

$$\left\{\frac{n-2}{5}\Delta + 1\right\}v_n = \beta_n,$$

so that Eq. (9–5) may be replaced by the three cascaded equations

$$\alpha_n = \alpha_{n-1} + \frac{3}{n+1}(u_n - \alpha_{n-1}),$$

$$\beta_n = \beta_{n-1} + \frac{4}{n+2}(\alpha_n - \beta_{n-1}), \qquad (9\text{–}6)$$

$$v_n = v_{n-1} + \frac{5}{n+3}(\beta_n - v_{n-1}).$$

9.6 A discrete scheme with additional features. A scheme for processing discrete-time radar tracking data which has potentially all of the practical features of the variable discrete schemes described in this chapter and, in addition, provides a running account of the average square of the deviations from the least squares regression curve and which is not restricted to uniform sampling intervals is described by Levine (1961).

CHAPTER 10

MEASUREMENT OF POWER SPECTRA

After a practical data-smoothing scheme (with or without prediction, delay-correction, or retrodiction) has been designed, we may wish to determine how well it would perform with the actual noise and perhaps also to determine how far short its performance is from that of a scheme which is optimum for the actual noise. In either case, it will usually be necessary to measure the actual noise spectrum.

In two cases of experience it was found that the actual noise spectrum had a strong sharp peak beyond the signal frequency band but close enough to require some additional measure of the type indicated in Section 10.13.

This final chapter is, therefore, devoted to a short version of *The Measurement of Power Spectra from the Point of View of Communications Engineering* by R. B. Blackman and J. W. Tukey (Dover, 1959), hereafter referred to as BT, supplemented by some additional material. It is motivated to some extent by comments received from some of the readers of the original account. Hence, some of the topics treated in BT will be treated here with additional details.†

10.1 Power spectrum analysis by instrumental methods (BT pp. 25–28, 112–116). A widely used instrumental method of power spectrum analysis is to apply the data to a bank of fixed narrow bandpass filters and to measure the average power output of each filter. Let us determine the relation of the average power output of a typical filter to the true power spectrum.

In Fig. 10.1, SRP stands for a stationary random process which generates the random function $X(t)$ continuously over an indefinite length of time. The switch is symbolic of the essential circumstance that only a finite segment of $X(t)$ is available for spectral analysis. In order to simplify the use of Fourier transformations we will represent the data by $B(t)X(t)$, defined over all values of t in $-\infty < t < \infty$, where

$$B(t) = 1 \qquad \text{for } 0 < t < T,$$
$$= 0 \qquad \text{otherwise.} \tag{10-1}$$

The function $B(t)$ is a *data window*; in particular here, a rectangular data window.

---

† On the other hand, the present account contains nothing corresponding to:
BT pp. 1–11, Introduction to Part I,
BT pp. 83–90, Introduction to Part II,
BT pp. 54–66, Planning for Measurement (in Part I),
BT pp. 147–159, Details for Planning (in Part II),
BT pp. 66–82, Appendix A, Fundamental Fourier Techniques.

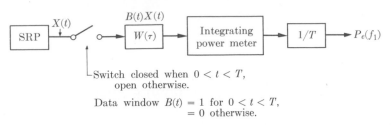

Switch closed when $0 < t < T$,
open otherwise.

Data window $B(t) = 1$ for $0 < t < T$,
                $= 0$ otherwise.

FIG. 10.1. Instrumental measurement of power spectrum.

The function $B(t)X(t)$ is applied to a filter which has a narrow passband centered at a frequency of f_1 cycles/sec. The output of the filter is represented by

$$V(t) = \int W(t - \lambda)B(\lambda)X(\lambda)\, d\lambda, \tag{10-2}$$

where $W(\tau)$ is the weighting function of the filter. (The range of all integrals is $-\infty$ to $+\infty$ unless otherwise indicated.) The output of the filter is applied to an energy meter (that is, an integrating power meter) whose final reading (after having essentially ceased to increase, at some $t > T$) is divided by T to give the *power estimate*

$$P_e(f_1) = \frac{1}{T} \int [V(t)]^2\, dt. \tag{10-3}$$

If this procedure could be repeated an indefinite number of times, we would have an *ensemble* of values of $P_e(f_1)$. From a statistical point of view, we are interested in how the

ensemble average, ave $\{P_e(f_1)\}$,

and the

ensemble variance, var $\{P_e(f_1)\}$,

are related to the

true power spectrum, $P(f)$.

Let us consider the ensemble average. Using a well-known device of expressing the product of integrals (or powers of an integral) as a multiple integral, we have, by Eqs. (10–2) and (10–3),

$$P_e(f_1) = \frac{1}{T} \iiint W(t - \lambda_1)W(t - \lambda_2)B(\lambda_1)B(\lambda_2)X(\lambda_1)X(\lambda_2)\, d\lambda_1\, d\lambda_2\, dt.$$

Since

$$\text{ave } \{X(\lambda_1)X(\lambda_2)\} = C(\lambda_1 - \lambda_2),$$

where $C(\tau)$ is the true *autocovariance* for time shift (lead or lag) τ, then

$$\text{ave } \{P_e(f_1)\} = \frac{1}{T} \iiint W(t - \lambda_1)W(t - \lambda_2)B(\lambda_1)B(\lambda_2)C(\lambda_1 - \lambda_2)\, d\lambda_1\, d\lambda_2\, dt.$$

Making the substitutions

$$C(\lambda_1 - \lambda_2) = \int P(f)e^{i\omega(\lambda_1 - \lambda_2)}\, df \qquad (\omega = 2\pi f),$$

$$W(t - \lambda_1) = \int Y(f')e^{i\omega'(t-\lambda_1)}\, df' \qquad (\omega' = 2\pi f'),$$

$$W(t - \lambda_2) = \int Y(f'')e^{i\omega''(t-\lambda_2)}\, df'' \qquad (\omega'' = 2\pi f''),$$

followed by the substitutions

$$\int e^{i(\omega' + \omega'')t}\, dt = \delta(f' + f''),$$

$$\int B(\lambda_1)e^{-i(\omega'-\omega)\lambda_1}\, d\lambda_1 = J(f' - f),$$

$$\int B(\lambda_2)e^{-i(\omega''+\omega)\lambda_2}\, d\lambda_2 = J(f'' + f),$$

and then integrating with respect to f'', we get

$$\text{ave}\ \{P_e(f_1)\} = \frac{1}{T}\iint J(f' - f)J(f - f')Y(f')Y(-f')P(f)\, df'\, df$$

$$= \int_0^\infty H(f)P(f)\, df, \tag{10-4}$$

where

$$H(f) = \frac{2}{T}\int |J(f - f')|^2 |Y(f')|^2\, df'$$

$$= \frac{2}{T}|J(f)|^2 * |Y(f)|^2. \tag{10-5}$$

(The asterisk is the conventional notation for convolution.)

From the way in which $H(f)$ occurs in Eq. (10–4), it is the *effective power transfer function* as far as ave $\{P_e(f_1)\}$ is concerned. It is occasionally called a "spectral window," but this term is usually reserved for a frequency function which is convolved with the true power spectrum, as in Eq. (10–10), further on. Since the effective power transfer function $H(f)$ is the convolution of the filter power transfer function $|Y(f)|^2$ with

$$\frac{2}{T}|J(f)|^2 = 2T\left[\frac{\sin (\omega T/2)}{(\omega T/2)}\right]^2$$

(see Fig. 10.2), it is clear that the resolving power of the filter will not be very effective unless $1/T$ is much smaller than the filter bandwidth.†

---

† The term "resolving power" is used here with the same connotation as in optical imagery where, by Rayleigh's criterion, the images of two object points are regarded as just resolved if the central maximum of the diffraction pattern of one image coincides with the first null away from the central maximum of the diffraction pattern of the other image (Sears, 1949; O'Neill, 1963).

In a strict statistical sense, since

$$\text{ave }\{P_e(f_1)\} \neq P(f_1),$$

$P_e(f_1)$ is usually a biased estimate of $P(f_1)$. It is, of course, an unbiased estimate of ave $\{P_e(f_1)\}$. That this may be very different from $P(f_1)$ is evident in the following example. Let the filter be ideally sharp so that

$$|Y(f)|^2 = \tfrac{1}{2}[\delta(f + f_1) + \delta(f - f_1)], \qquad (10\text{--}6)$$

and therefore

$$H(f) = \frac{1}{T}\{|J(f + f_1)|^2 + |J(f - f_1)|^2\}. \qquad (10\text{--}7)$$

If the true spectrum has a very high narrow peak at $f_1 + 3/(2T)$ cycles/sec as shown in Fig. 10.3, then $P_e(f_1)$ may depend more strongly on $P(f_1 + 3/(2T))$ than on $P(f_1)$.

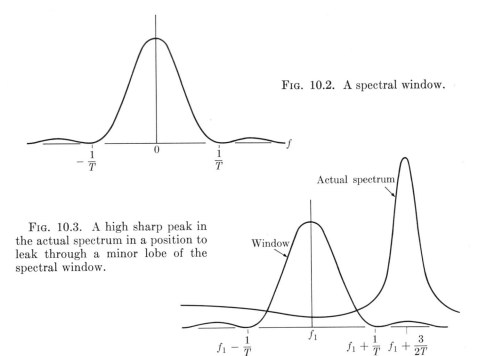

Fig. 10.2. A spectral window.

Fig. 10.3. A high sharp peak in the actual spectrum in a position to leak through a minor lobe of the spectral window.

The relation of var $\{P_e(f_1)\}$ to $P(f)$ will be covered later.

Another instrumental method frequently used in power spectrum analysis is to apply the recorded data to the filter as a periodic function with a period equal to the length of the record and to measure the steady-state power output of the filter. In this case, since the input power is concentrated at integral multiples of $1/T$ cycles/sec, it is sufficient for our purposes to determine the relation of the average input power at each of these frequencies to the true power spectrum.

The periodic input to the filter may be represented as a Fourier series of the form

$$F(t) = \sum_{-\infty}^{\infty} A_n e^{i2\pi n t/T},$$

where

$$A_n = \frac{1}{T} \int B(t) X(t) e^{-i2\pi n t/T} \, dt.$$

The power at $f = n/T$ in the two-sided discrete power spectrum is

$$|A_n|^2 = \frac{1}{T^2} \iint B(t_1) B(t_2) X(t_1) X(t_2) e^{-i2\pi n(t_1 - t_2)/T} \, dt_1 \, dt_2.$$

Hence, over the ensemble of values of $|A_n|^2$,

$$\text{ave } \{|A_n|^2\} = \frac{1}{T^2} \iint B(t_1) B(t_2) C(t_1 - t_2) e^{-i2\pi n(t_1 - t_2)/T} \, dt_1 \, dt_2.$$

Making the substitution

$$C(t_1 - t_2) = \int P(f) e^{i\omega(t_1 - t_2)} \, df \qquad (\omega = 2\pi f),$$

followed by the substitutions

$$\int B(t_1) e^{-i((2\pi n/T) - \omega) t_1} \, dt_1 = J\left(\frac{n}{T} - f\right),$$

$$\int B(t_2) e^{-i(\omega - (2\pi n/T)) t_2} \, dt_2 = J\left(f - \frac{n}{T}\right),$$

we get

$$\text{ave } \{|A_n|^2\} = \frac{2}{T^2} \int_0^\infty \left| J\left(f - \frac{n}{T}\right) \right|^2 P(f) \, df. \tag{10–8}$$

Thus, a situation similar to that shown in Fig. 10.3 can occur in which $|A_n|^2$ depends more strongly on $P[(n/T) + (3/2T)]$ than on $P(n/T)$.

In either of the two methods considered here, some advantage may be gained by *shaping* the data window $B(t)$ in the range $0 < t < T$. It is possible in this way to reduce the size of the side-lobes of $J(f)$ relative to the size of the main lobe, at the price of increasing the frequency interval covered by the main lobe. It is not possible to eliminate the side lobes entirely because of the requirement that $B(t) = 0$ outside of the interval $0 < t < T$. Thus, the attainable resolving power depends on the available length of data as well as the bandwidth of the filter.

10.2 Hypothetical direct numerical power spectrum analysis (BT pp. 93–95). The term "hypothetical" refers to the fact that the method involves integrals (which are, strictly, not computable numerically) and the term "direct" to the fact that the spectral density estimates are computed directly from the data, perhaps with a shaped data window. Thus, let

$$P_i(f_1) = \frac{1}{T}\left|\int B_i(t)X(t)e^{-i\omega_1 t}\,dt\right|^2 \qquad (\omega_1 = 2\pi f_1), \qquad (10\text{–}9)$$

where $B_i(t) = 0$ outside of $0 < t < T$. Putting this in the form

$$P_i(f_1) = \frac{1}{T}\iint B_i(t_1)B_i(t_2)X(t_1)X(t_2)e^{-i\omega_1(t_1-t_2)}\,dt_1\,dt_2,$$

we get

$$\text{ave } \{P_i(f_1)\} = \frac{1}{T}\iint B_i(t_1)B_i(t_2)C(t_1-t_2)e^{-i\omega_1(t_1-t_2)}\,dt_1\,dt_2.$$

Making the substitution

$$C(t_1 - t_2) = \int P(f)e^{i\omega(t_1-t_2)}\,df,$$

followed by the substitutions

$$\int B_i(t_1)e^{-i(\omega_1-\omega)t_1}\,dt_1 = J_i(f_1 - f),$$

$$\int B_i(t_2)e^{-i(\omega-\omega_1)t_2}\,dt_2 = J_i(f - f_1),$$

we get

$$\text{ave } \{P_i(f_1)\} = \frac{1}{T}\int |J_i(f_1 - f)|^2 P(f)\,df$$

or

$$\text{ave } \{P_i(f_1)\} = Q_i(f) * P(f), \qquad (10\text{–}10)$$

where

$$Q_i(f) = \frac{1}{T}|J_i(f)|^2. \qquad (10\text{–}11)$$

The function $Q_i(f)$, which is convolved with the true spectrum, is a *spectral window*.

Any equation of the form

$$\text{ave } \{P_i(f_1)\} = \int Q_i(f_1 - f)P(f)\,df \qquad (10\text{–}12)$$

may be expressed in the form

$$\text{ave } \{P_i(f_1)\} = \int_0^\infty H_i(f;f_1)P(f)\,df, \qquad (10\text{–}13)$$

where the following relation holds:

$$H_i(f;f_1) = Q_i(f_1 + f) + Q_i(f_1 - f). \tag{10-14}$$

The function $H_i(f;f_1)$, which is an even function of f, is the *effective power transfer function*. Equation (10–13) with Eqs. (10–14) and (10–11) is of course the same as Eq. (10–4) with Eq. (10–7). If $B_i(t) = 1$ in $0 < t < T$, then

$$Q_i(f) = T\left[\frac{\sin (\omega T/2)}{(\omega T/2)}\right]^2,$$

as in Figs. 10.2 and 10.3.

10.3 Hypothetical indirect numerical power spectrum analysis (BT pp. 11–25, 90–93). This method, like the preceding one, is "hypothetical" because it involves integrals, but it is "indirect" because spectral density estimates are computed from a *modified apparent autocovariance* function.

Here we assume that the random function $X(t)$ is given in $-T_n/2 \le t \le T_n/2$ and that spectral density estimates are computed essentially according to the following procedure.

1. Compute the *apparent autocovariance*

$$C_{00}(\tau) = \frac{1}{2L(\tau)} \int_{-L(\tau)}^{L(\tau)} X\left(t - \frac{\tau}{2}\right) X\left(t + \frac{\tau}{2}\right) dt, \qquad L(\tau) = \frac{T_n - |\tau|}{2},$$

for $|\tau| \le T_m$, where $T_m < T_n$. (The *apparent autocovariance* is computable up to $|\tau| = T_n$, but in order to get reasonably stable power density estimates we will usually not want to use $C_{00}(\tau)$ beyond $|\tau| = T_n/10$.)

2. Compute the *modified apparent autocovariance*

$$C_i(\tau) - D_i(\tau)C_{00}(\tau)$$

where $D_i(\tau)$ is a *lag window* with the following properties:

$$D_i(0) = 1, \qquad D_i(-\tau) = D_i(\tau),$$
$$D_i(\tau) \equiv 0 \qquad \text{for } |\tau| > T_m.$$

3. Compute spectral density estimates according to the formula

$$P_i(f_1) = \int C_i(\tau)e^{-i\omega_1\tau} d\tau.$$

To determine the relation of ave $\{P_i(f_1)\}$ to the true power spectrum $P(f)$ we first note that

$$\text{ave } \{C_i(\tau)\} = D_i(\tau)C(\tau)$$

for all values of τ in $-\infty < \tau < \infty$. Since

$$P_i(f) = \mathfrak{F}[C_i(\tau)],$$

where $\mathfrak{F}$ stands for the Fourier transform, we get

$$\begin{aligned}
\text{ave } \{P_i(f)\} &= \mathfrak{F}[\text{ave } \{C_i(\tau)\}] \\
&= \mathfrak{F}[D_i(\tau)C(\tau)] \\
&= Q_i(f) * P(f),
\end{aligned} \tag{10–15}$$

where the *spectral window* $Q_i(f)$ is given by

$$Q_i(f) = \mathfrak{F}[D_i(\tau)]. \tag{10–16}$$

Again, we may write

$$\text{ave } \{P_i(f_1)\} = \int_0^\infty H_i(f;f_1)P(f) \, df, \tag{10–17}$$

where the *effective power transfer function* $H_i(f;f_1)$ is given by

$$H_i(f;f_1) = Q_i(f + f_1) + Q_i(f - f_1). \tag{10–18}$$

10.4 Lag and spectral windows (BT pp. 95–100). The simplest lag window is

$$\begin{aligned}
D_0(\tau) &= 1 \quad &\text{for } |\tau| < T_m \\
&= 0 \quad &\text{for } |\tau| > T_m,
\end{aligned} \tag{10–19}$$

and the corresponding spectral window is

$$Q_0(f) = 2T_m \frac{\sin \omega T_m}{\omega T_m} \quad (\omega = 2\pi f). \tag{10–20}$$

This (simple) window-pair is illustrated in Fig. 10.4.

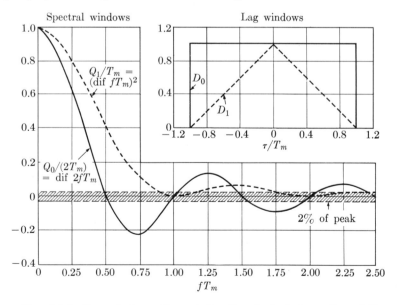

FIG. 10.4. Lag windows D_0 and D_1. Spectral windows Q_0 and Q_1.

A form of lag window (due essentially to Bartlett) which is sometimes used implicitly when $T_m = T_n$ because it simplifies the computation of $C_{00}(\tau)$ is

$$D_1(\tau) = 1 - \frac{|\tau|}{T_m} \qquad \text{for } |\tau| < T_m$$

$$= 0 \qquad \text{for } |\tau| > T_m. \tag{10-21}$$

The corresponding spectral window is

$$Q_1(f) = T_m \left[\frac{\sin (\omega T_m/2)}{(\omega T_m/2)} \right]^2. \tag{10-22}$$

This window-pair is also illustrated in Fig. 10.4.

A spectral window which is better than $Q_1(f)$, in the sense of having smaller side lobes, is based on the lag window

$$D_2(\tau) = \frac{1}{2} \left(1 + \cos \frac{\pi \tau}{T_m} \right) D_0(\tau). \tag{10-23}$$

The corresponding spectral window is

$$Q_2(f) = \left[\tfrac{1}{2}\delta(f) + \tfrac{1}{4}\delta\left(f + \frac{1}{2T_m}\right) + \tfrac{1}{4}\delta\left(f - \frac{1}{2T_m}\right) \right] * Q_0(f)$$

$$= \tfrac{1}{2}Q_0(f) + \tfrac{1}{4}Q_0\left(f + \frac{1}{2T_m}\right) + \tfrac{1}{4}Q_0\left(f - \frac{1}{2T_m}\right). \tag{10-24}$$

This window-pair is illustrated in Fig. 10.5.

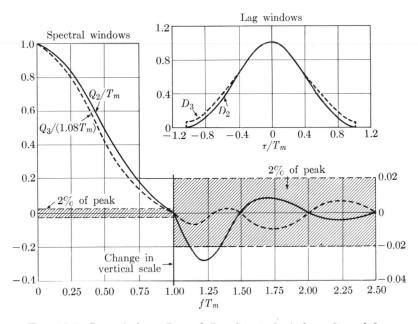

FIG. 10.5. Lag windows D_2 and D_3. Spectral windows Q_2 and Q_3.

A spectral window, which is better than $Q_1(f)$ and better than $Q_2(f)$ in the side lobe range $1/T_m < |f| < 2/T_m$, but not quite as good as $Q_2(f)$ further out from the main lobe is based on the lag window

$$D_3(\tau) = \left(0.54 + 0.46 \cos \frac{\pi\tau}{T_m}\right) D_0(\tau). \qquad (10\text{-}25)$$

The corresponding spectral window is

$$Q_3(f) = \left[0.54\delta(f) + 0.23\delta\left(f + \frac{1}{2T_m}\right) + 0.23\delta\left(f - \frac{1}{2T_m}\right)\right] * Q_0(f)$$

$$= 0.54Q_0(f) + 0.23Q_0\left(f + \frac{1}{2T_m}\right) + 0.23Q_0\left(f - \frac{1}{2T_m}\right). \quad (10\text{-}26)$$

This window-pair is also illustrated in Fig. 10.5.

A better comparison of these four spectral windows (plotted in db loss) is shown in Fig. 10.6.

It should be noted that $Q_0(f)$, $Q_2(f)$, and $Q_3(f)$ have negative side lobes so that spectral density estimates based on these spectral windows, especially $Q_0(f)$, may be occasionally negative. However, D. R. Brillinger has called the author's attention to the fact that the occurrence of negative spectral density estimates in the *indirect* power spectrum analysis is usually due to, and is therefore a useful indication of, the presence of a strong sharp peak which is not resolvable except by increasing T_n and T_m.

Other forms of lag windows and spectral windows were considered in Bartlett (1955), Parzen (1957), Grenander and Rosenblatt (1957).

10.5 Smoothing simple estimates. In view of the relation between $D_2(\tau)$ and $D_0(\tau)$ and the corresponding relation between $Q_2(f)$ and $Q_0(f)$, there is no need to introduce $D_2(\tau)$ explicitly into the hypothetical procedure outlined above before Fourier transformation. Since

$$P_2(f) = \mathfrak{F}[C_2(\tau)]$$
$$= \mathfrak{F}[D_2(\tau)C_{00}(\tau)]$$
$$= \mathfrak{F}\left[\frac{1}{2}\left(1 + \cos \frac{\pi\tau}{T_m}\right) D_0(\tau)C_{00}(\tau)\right]$$
$$= \mathfrak{F}\left[\frac{1}{2}\left(1 + \cos \frac{\pi\tau}{T_m}\right) C_0(\tau)\right]$$
$$= \nabla_{hn}(f) * P_0(f),$$

where

$$\nabla_{hn}(f) = \tfrac{1}{2}\delta(f) + \tfrac{1}{4}\delta\left(f + \frac{1}{2T_m}\right) + \tfrac{1}{4}\delta\left(f - \frac{1}{2T_m}\right),$$

we may compute the simple spectral density estimates $P_0(f_1)$, and then the

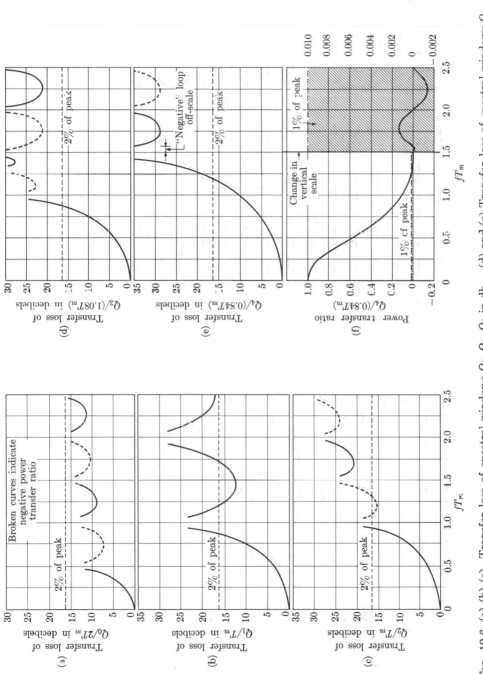

FIG. 10.6. (a) (b) (c) Transfer loss of spectral windows Q_0, Q_1, Q_2 in db. (d) and (e) Transfer loss of spectral windows Q_3, Q_4 in db. (f) Power transfer ratio of spectral window Q_4

smoothed estimates

$$P_2(f_1) = \tfrac{1}{4}P_0\left(f_1 - \frac{1}{2T_m}\right) + \tfrac{1}{2}P_0(f_1) + \tfrac{1}{4}P_0\left(f_1 + \frac{1}{2T_m}\right). \quad (10\text{--}27)$$

This method of smoothing (convolution), with weights 0.25, 0.50, 0.25, is called *hanning* after the Austrian meteorologist Julius von Hann.

Similarly, since

$$P_3(f) = \nabla_{hm}(f) * P_0(f),$$

where

$$\nabla_{hm}(f) = 0.54\delta(f) + 0.23\delta\left(f + \frac{1}{2T_m}\right) + 0.23\delta\left(f - \frac{1}{2T_m}\right),$$

we may compute the simple spectral density estimates $P_0(f_1)$ and then the smoothed estimates

$$P_3(f_1) = 0.23P_0\left(f_1 - \frac{1}{2T_m}\right) + 0.54P_0(f_1) + 0.23P_0\left(f_1 + \frac{1}{2T_m}\right). \quad (10\text{--}28)$$

This method of smoothing (convolution), with weights 0.23, 0.54, 0.23, is called *hamming* after R. W. Hamming.

The lag window defined by

$$D_4(\tau) = \left(0.42 + 0.50 \cos\frac{\pi\tau}{T_m} + 0.08 \cos\frac{2\pi\tau}{T_m}\right) D_0(\tau),$$

for which the corresponding spectral window $Q_4(f)$ is plotted in Fig. 10.6, is easily shown to be expressible in the form

$$D_4(\tau) = \left[\frac{1}{25}\left(17 + 8\cos\frac{\pi\tau}{T_m}\right)\right]\left[\frac{1}{2}\left(1 + \cos\frac{\pi\tau}{T_m}\right)\right] D_0(\tau). \quad (10\text{--}29)$$

Hence, the spectral density estimates $P_4(f_1)$, which would be obtained by using the lag window $D_4(\tau)$, may be obtained from the simple estimates $P_0(f_1)$ by first *hanning* to obtain the smoothed estimates $P_2(f_1)$ and then smoothing once more in accordance with the formula

$$P_4(f_1) = 0.16P_2\left(f_1 - \frac{1}{2T_m}\right) + 0.68P_2(f_1) + 0.16P_2\left(f_1 + \frac{1}{2T_m}\right). \quad (10\text{--}30)$$

This second smoothing is a convolution with weights 0.16, 0.68, 0.16.

Thus, an advantage of the "indirect" method of power spectrum analysis is the facility of effectively changing the lag window (within a class of such windows) after Fourier transformation. This advantage holds over into the case of finite-length discrete-time data.

10.6 Covariability—basic formula (BT pp. 100–103).   A basic relation of cov $\{P_i(f_1), P_j(f_2)\}$ to the true power spectrum $P(f)$ is derived in BT pp. 100–103. However, that derivation omits a fairly elusive detail. To supply that detail here let us recall that, by definition,

$$\text{cov } \{x, y,\} = \text{ave } \{(x - \bar{x})(y - \bar{y})\},$$

where for convenience we have written $\bar{x}$ and $\bar{y}$ for ave $\{x\}$ and ave $\{y\}$, respectively. Thus,

$$\text{cov } \{x, y\} = \text{ave } \{xy\} - \text{ave } \{x\} \text{ ave } \{y\}.$$

Then,

$$
\begin{aligned}
\text{cov } \{P_i(f_1), P_j(f_2)\} &= \text{ave } \{P_i(f_1)P_j(f_2)\} - \text{ave } \{P_i(f_1)\} \text{ ave } \{P_j(f_2)\} \\
&= \text{ave } \left\{\iint C_i(\tau_1)C_j(\tau_2) \cos \omega_1\tau_1 \cos \omega_2\tau_2 \, d\tau_1 \, d\tau_2\right\} \\
&\quad - \text{ave } \left\{\int C_i(\tau_1) \cos \omega_1\tau_1 \, d\tau_1\right\} \text{ ave } \left\{\int C_j(\tau_2) \cos \omega_2\tau_2 \, d\tau_2\right\} \\
&= \iint \left[\text{ave } \{C_i(\tau_1)C_j(\tau_2)\} - \text{ave } \{C_i(\tau_1)\} \text{ ave } \{C_j(\tau_2)\}\right] \\
&\qquad\qquad\qquad\qquad\qquad\quad \times \cos \omega_1\tau_1 \cos \omega_2\tau_2 \, d\tau_1 \, d\tau_2 \\
&= \iint \left[\text{ave } \{C_0(\tau_1)C_0(\tau_2)\} - \text{ave } \{C_0(\tau_1)\} \text{ ave } \{C_0(\tau_2)\}\right] \\
&\qquad\qquad\qquad \times D_i(\tau_1)D_j(\tau_2) \cos \omega_1\tau_1 \cos \omega_2\tau_2 \, d\tau_1 \, d\tau_2 \\
&= \iint \text{cov } \{C_0(\tau_1), C_0(\tau_2)\} D_i(\tau_1)D_j(\tau_2) \cos \omega_1\tau_1 \\
&\qquad\qquad\qquad\qquad\qquad\qquad\qquad \times \cos \omega_2\tau_2 \, d\tau_1 \, d\tau_2.
\end{aligned}
$$

Thus, we need cov $\{C_0(\tau_1), C_0(\tau_2)\}$. For convenience, we now write

$$C_0(\tau) = \frac{1}{2L(\tau)} \int_{-L(\tau)}^{L(\tau)} M(t, \tau) \, dt,$$

where $M(t, \tau) = X(t - (\tau/2))X(t + (\tau/2))$ and $L(\tau) = (T_n - |\tau|)/2$. Then, by a routine similar to the one used above, we get

cov $\{C_0(\tau_1), C_0(\tau_2)\}$

$$= \frac{1}{4L(\tau_1)L(\tau_2)} \int_{-L(\tau_1)}^{L(\tau_1)} \int_{-L(\tau_2)}^{L(\tau_2)} \text{cov } \{M(t_1, \tau_1), M(t_2, \tau_2)\} \, dt_1 \, dt_2.$$

Thus, we need cov $\{M(t_1, \tau_1), M(t_2, \tau_2)\}$ or cov $\{wx, yz\}$, where

$$w = X\left(t_1 - \frac{\tau_1}{2}\right), \quad x = X\left(t_1 + \frac{\tau_1}{2}\right),$$

$$y = X\left(t_2 - \frac{\tau_2}{2}\right), \quad z = X\left(t_2 + \frac{\tau_2}{2}\right).$$

This is where the derivation starts in BT p. 100. The derivation assumes that $X(t)$ is Gaussian with zero average.

In the course of the derivation it becomes evident that the result of integration with respect to τ_1 and τ_2 would be much simpler to interpret if the limits of integration with respect to t_1 and t_2 were independent of τ_1 and τ_2. Such independence could be achieved if $C_0(\tau)$ were actually computed according to

$$C_0(\tau) = \frac{1}{T_m} \int_{-T_m/2}^{T_m/2} X\left(t - \frac{\tau}{2}\right) X\left(t + \frac{\tau}{2}\right) dt \qquad |\tau| \le T_m,$$

(in effect, using the Bartlett window D_1 if $T_m = T_n$) but this would sacrifice some of the stability of $C_0(\tau)$ at low values of τ. A compromise (with little sacrifice in accuracy) is struck by assuming that the original definition of $C_0(\tau)$ is approximately equivalent to

$$C_0'(\tau) = \frac{1}{T_n'} \int_{-T_n'/2}^{T_n'/2} X\left(t - \frac{\tau}{2}\right) X\left(t + \frac{\tau}{2}\right) dt,$$

where

$$T_n' = T_n - \frac{\int_0^{T_m} \tau D_i(\tau)\, d\tau}{\int_0^{T_m} D_i(\tau)\, d\tau}.$$

The second term in the right-hand member of the last equation turns out to be $0.50\, T_m$, $0.33\, T_m$, $0.30\, T_m$, and $0.33\, T_m$ for $i = 0, 1, 2, 3$ respectively. Hence, another compromise is struck by taking

$$T_n' = T_n - \frac{T_m}{3}.$$

Without going any further into the details of the derivation (which are given in BT pp. 100–103), the result is that

$$\text{cov } \{P_i(f_1), P_j(f_2)\} = \frac{1}{4} \int H_i(f;f_1) H_j(f;f_2) \Gamma(f)\, df, \qquad (10\text{–}31)$$

where

$$\Gamma(f) = 4 \int P(f + f') P(f - f') \left(\frac{\sin \omega' T_n'}{\omega' T_n'}\right)^2 df'. \qquad (10\text{–}32)$$

The function $\Gamma(f)$ is called the *power-variance spectrum*. It is associated not only with the covariance of the estimates $P_i(f_1)$ and $P_j(f_2)$, but also with the variance

$$\text{var } \{P_i(f_1)\} = \frac{1}{4} \int [H_i(f;f_1)]^2 \Gamma(f)\, df, \qquad (10\text{–}33)$$

just as the true power spectrum $P(f)$ is associated with the average

$$\text{ave } \{P_i(f_1)\} = \frac{1}{2} \int H_i(f;f_1) P(f)\, df. \qquad (10\text{–}34)$$

A measure of the stability of the spectral density estimate $P_i(f_1)$ about ave $\{P_i(f_1)\}$ is the dimensionless ratio

$$k = \frac{2[\text{ave } \{P_i(f_1)\}]^2}{\text{var } \{P_i(f_1)\}}$$

which is called *degrees of freedom* not only because of the formal analogy to the corresponding relation in the case of chi-square variates, but also because further theoretical study and experimental investigations with artificially generated time series show a close quantitative agreement.

10.7 Covariability—approximations (BT pp. 103–112). The formulas for the average, variance, and covariance of spectral density estimates given above are not useful in practice because they involve the true power spectrum which is unknown. The material in BT pp. 103–112 is, therefore, concerned with the study of special cases with the object of discovering a practical approximate formula for *degrees of freedom* which does not involve the true power spectrum.

Let us first consider a special case which should be avoided in practice, if possible, by careful planning of the data-acquisition phase of a measurement program. Let us assume that the true power spectrum consists only of a very sharp peak (width $\ll 1/T'_n$) at $f = f_0$ and its mathematical image at $f = -f_0$. Then, as far as $\Gamma(f)$ is concerned,

$$P(f) \approx \delta(f + f_0) + \delta(f - f_0),$$

and therefore

$$\Gamma(f) \approx 2\left[\delta(f + f_0) + \delta(f - f_0) + 2\left(\frac{\sin \omega_0 T'_n}{\omega_0 T'_n}\right)^2 \delta(f)\right].$$

Hence

$$\text{var } \{P_i(f_1)\} = |H_i(f_0;f_1)|^2 + |H_i(0;f_1)|^2 \left(\frac{\sin \omega_0 T'_n}{\omega_0 T'_n}\right)^2$$

while, of course,

$$\text{ave } \{P_i(f_1)\} = H_i(f_0;f_1).$$

Thus,

$$k = \frac{2}{1 + \left[\dfrac{H_i(0;f_1)}{H_i(f_0;f_1)}\dfrac{\sin \omega_0 T'_n}{\omega_0 T'_n}\right]^2}.$$

This cannot exceed 2, and reduces to only 1 when $f_1 = f_0 = 0$. Difficulties associated with the presence of one or more quite narrow and very high peaks in the true spectrum will require special measures such as those suggested in BT pp. 42–43.

Let us now start on a more fruitful series of approximations. In the first place we note that $P(f + f')P(f - f')$ is an even function of f' so that its Taylor series expansion in terms of f' does not contain odd powers of f'. We suspect, therefore, that $\Gamma(f)$ will not be very sensitive to the slope of $P(f)$ at $f = f$ provided that this slope is approximately constant over an interval of width

$1/T'_n$ centered on $\hat{f} = f$. Thus, let

$$P(f + f') = P(f)(1 + 2\beta f' T'_n) \qquad |\beta| \leq 1,$$

and let us use the approximation

$$\left(\frac{\sin \omega' T'_n}{\omega' T'_n}\right)^2 \approx \frac{35}{32}\left[1 - (2f' T'_n)^2\right]^3 \qquad |f'| < \frac{1}{2T_n},$$

$$\approx 0 \qquad\qquad\qquad |f'| > \frac{1}{2T'_n},$$

where the factor 35/32 preserves the area. We then readily find that

$$\Gamma(f) = \frac{2}{T'_n}[P(f)]^2 \left(1 - \frac{\beta^2}{9}\right) \qquad |\beta| \leq 1.$$

Under the stated conditions, therefore, we have the interim result

$$k \approx T'_n \frac{[\int H_i(f;f_1)P(f)\,df]}{\int [H_i(f;f_1)P(f)]^2\,df},$$

which still involves the true power spectrum.

Before we take the next step of approximation it is of some interest to relate this interim result with ordinary sampling theory. Thus,

1. If x is a Gaussian variate with ave $\{x\} = 0$ and var $\{x\} = \sigma^2$, then ave $\{x^2\} = \sigma^2$ and ave $\{x^4\} = 3\sigma^4$, whence var $\{x^2\} = 2\sigma^4$.

2. If $y = x_1^2 + x_2^2 + \cdots + x_n^2$, where the x_i's are independent Gaussian variates, with ave $\{x_i\} = 0$ and var $\{x_i\} = 1$ for every i, then y is a "chi-square variate on n degrees of freedom." Since averages are additive and variances are additive under independence, then ave $\{y\} = n$ and var $\{y\} = 2n$, whence

$$\frac{2[\text{ave }\{y\}]^2}{\text{var }\{y\}} = n.$$

3. If var $\{x_i\} = \sigma^2$ for every i, then y is a *multiple* of a chi-square on n degrees of freedom. Now, ave $\{y\} = n\sigma^2$ and var $\{y\} = 2n\sigma^4$, but

$$\frac{2[\text{ave }\{y\}]^2}{\text{var }\{y\}} = n,$$

as before.

4. If $z = h_1 y_1 + h_2 y_2 + \cdots + h_r y_r$, where the y_i's are multiples of independent chi-squares, with ave $\{y_i\} = n_i p_i$ and var $\{y_i\} = 2n_i p_i^2$ for each i, then

$$\text{ave }\{z\} = \sum n_i h_i p_i, \qquad \text{var }\{z\} = 2\sum n_i (h_i p_i)^2,$$

whence

$$\frac{2[\text{ave }\{z\}]^2}{\text{var }\{z\}} = \frac{[\sum n_i h_i p_i]^2}{\sum n_i (h_i p_i)^2} \qquad (= v, \text{ say}).$$

In particular, if $n_i = n$ for every i, then

$$v = n \frac{[\sum h_i p_i]^2}{\sum (h_i p_i)^2}.$$

If all $h_i p_i$ are equal, then z is a multiple of a chi-square on v degrees of freedom. If the $h_i p_i$ are different and in particular if there is even only one negative h_i, then z is not a multiple of a chi-square (there may be a finite probability that z will be negative). If the $h_i p_i$ are all nearly equal we may expect z to be nearly as stable as a chi-square on v degrees of freedom.

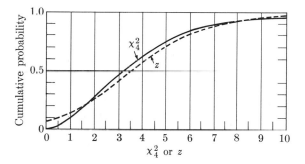

FIG. 10.7. Cumulative probability of a linear combination of chi-square variates.

A noteworthy fact, however, is that even when the $h_i p_i$ are quite different, z may be nearly as stable as a chi-square on v degrees of freedom. As an example, consider the case

$$z = -0.2y_1 + 0.6y_2 + 0.6y_3 - 0.2y_4$$

in which each y_i is a chi-square on 5 degrees of freedom. Since ave $\{y_i\} = 5$, and var $\{y_i\} = 10$, then ave $\{z\} = 4$, and var $\{z\} = 8$, whence $v = 4$. The broken curve in Fig. 10.7 is the cumulative probability distribution of z, while the continuous curve is the cumulative probability distribution of a chi-square on 4 degrees of freedom. There is a probability of 0.049 that z will be negative. The 90% confidence limits for z are 0 and 9.2, while those for the chi-square on 4 degrees of freedom are 0.7 and 9.5. Clearly, z is only slightly less stable than a chi-square on 4 degrees of freedom. For present purposes this difference may be neglected.†

A comparison of our interim formula for k and the formula for v suggests the partition of the frequency range $-\infty < f < \infty$ into *elementary bands* of width $1/T'_n$, with one band centered at $f = 0$, and the association of 1 degree of freedom with each band (see the parenthetical remark starting at the bottom of BT p. 111, regarding sharp peaks).

---

† Extensive analyses of this sort are given in Satterthwaite (1941) and Box (1954).

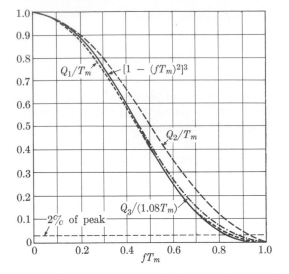

FIG. 10.8. Approximation to standard spectral windows.

Let us now consider the next approximation to the interim formula for k. The spectral windows $Q_1(f)$, $Q_2(f)$, and $Q_3(f)$ are closely approximated by

$$[1 - (T_m f)^2]^3 \qquad \text{for } |f| < \frac{1}{T_m},$$

$$\text{zero} \qquad \text{for } |f| > \frac{1}{T_m},$$

as shown in Fig. 10.8. (There is no need here to preserve areas.) If we introduce this approximation into

$$H_i(f; f_1) = Q_i(f + f_1) + Q_i(f - f_1),$$

assume for the time being that $f_1 \geq 1/T_m$ so that there is no overlapping of $Q_i(f + f_1)$ and $Q_i(f - f_1)$, and assume that

$$P(f) = P(f_1)[1 + \beta T_m(f - f_1)] \qquad |\beta| \leq 1,$$

within the frequency limits of $Q_i(f - f_1)$, then

$$k = \frac{429}{175[1 + (\beta^2/15)]} \frac{T'_n}{T_m}.$$

Thus,

$$2.30 \frac{T'_n}{T_m} \leq k \leq 2.45 \frac{T'_n}{T_m}.$$

A less favorable case is to assume that $P(f) = P(f_1)Q_i(f - f_1)$ within the frequency limits of the spectral window $Q_i(f - f_1)$. Then, $k = 1.90 \, T'_n/T_m$.

Hence, for practical use, we may take

$$k = 2\frac{T'_n}{T_m} = 2\left(\frac{T_n}{T_m} - \frac{1}{3}\right) \qquad f_1 \geq \frac{1}{T_m}. \tag{10-35}$$

This will be slightly pessimistic in almost all cases. If $f_1 < 1/T_m$, this should be multiplied by

$$\frac{1}{1 + \rho(f_1 T_m)},$$

as given in the following table.

TABLE 1

ξ	$\rho(\xi)$	$1/(1 + \rho)$
0	1	0.50
0.1	0.921	0.52
0.2	0.729	0.58
0.25	0.608	0.62
0.3	0.484	0.67
0.4	0.266	0.79
0.5	0.115	0.90
0.6	0.036	0.97
0.7	0.007	0.99
⋮	⋮	⋮
1.0	0	1

Incidentally, $\rho(\xi)$ is also the correlation coefficient between the spectral density estimate at f_1 and the spectral density estimate at $f_2 = f_1 + 2\xi/T_m$, for $f_1 \geq 1/T_m$ and $0 \leq \xi \leq 1$ for white noise. We will have occasion later on to refer to the values of $\rho(\xi)$ at $\xi = 0.25$ and 0.5.

10.8 Power spectrum analysis with finite-length discrete-time data (BT pp. 30–37, 52–54, 117–124). The direct method of power spectrum analysis with finite-length discrete-time data was not considered in BT, but it has been examined by Akcasu (1961) and by Welch (1961). Here, we will consider only the indirect method.

Assume that the data are represented by $n + 1$ consecutive values of $X(t)$, denoted by

$$X_0, X_1, \ldots, X_n$$

with uniform spacing of Δt. The spectral density estimates are then computed according to the following procedure.

1. Compute *mean lagged products* at spacing of $\Delta \tau = h\,\Delta t$,

$$C_r = \frac{1}{n - hr + 1} \sum_{q=0}^{n-hr} X_q X_{q+hr}, \qquad \left(r = 0, 1, \ldots, m, \text{ where } m \leq \frac{n}{h}\right).$$

If trends (zero-point bias and drift rate) are not removed from the data before computing mean lagged products, they should be removed before the next step in this procedure. This topic will be discussed later.

With regard to the ratio $\Delta\tau/\Delta t$, see the last paragraph under "Variability—Degrees of Freedom," below.

2. Compute *raw spectral density estimates* at frequency spacing of $1/(2m\,\Delta\tau)$,

$$V_s = \Delta\tau\left[C_0 + 2\sum_{r=1}^{m-1} C_r \cos\frac{rs\pi}{m} + C_m \cos s\pi\right] \qquad (s = 0, 1, \ldots, m).$$

This formula is equivalent to the standard Fourier transformation

$$\hat{V}(f) = \int \hat{C}(\tau)e^{-i\omega\tau}\,d\tau \qquad (\omega = 2\pi f),$$

where

$$\hat{C} = \Delta\tau\left[\tfrac{1}{2}C_{-m}\delta(\tau + m\,\Delta\tau) + \sum_{r=-m+1}^{r=m-1} C_r\delta(\tau - r\,\Delta\tau) + \tfrac{1}{2}C_m\delta(\tau - m\,\Delta\tau)\right],$$

$$C_{-r} = C_r \qquad \text{and} \qquad V_s = \hat{V}(s/2m\,\Delta\tau).$$

3. Compute *refined spectral density estimates*, U_s at frequency spacing of $1/(2m\,\Delta\tau)$ by smoothing (convolving) the raw estimates with the weights

$$0.25,\, 0.50,\, 0,25 \qquad \text{(hanning)},$$

or with the weights

$$0.23,\, 0.54,\, 0.23 \qquad \text{(hamming)},$$

taking $V_{-1} = V_1$ and $V_{m+1} = V_{m-1}$.

The refined estimates obtained by "hanning" the raw estimates may be further refined by convolving them with the weights 0.16, 0.68, 0.16, as described at the end of Section 10.5. However, the formula for "degrees of freedom" should be modified for this case.†

4. Double the refined estimates if they are to conform to the conventional one-sided definition of power spectra.

To determine the relation of ave $\{U_s\}$ to $P(f)$ we proceed very much as we did for the "hypothetical power spectrum analysis—indirect method." We have

$$\text{ave } \{C_r\} = C(r\,\Delta\tau)$$

so that

$$\text{ave } \{V_s\} = \Delta\tau\left[C(0) + 2\sum_{r=1}^{m-1} C(r\,\Delta\tau)\cos\frac{rs\pi}{m} + C(m\,\Delta\tau)\cos s\pi\right].$$

---

† Other weights have been proposed by Parzen (1957, 1961) and Jenkins (1961, 1963).

This may be expressed as a Fourier *integral*,

$$\text{ave } \{V_s\} = \int \nabla_m(\tau;\Delta\tau)C(\tau)e^{-i\omega\tau}\, d\tau \qquad \omega = \frac{\pi s}{m\,\Delta\tau},$$

where

$$\nabla_m(\tau;\Delta\tau) = \Delta\tau\left[\tfrac{1}{2}\delta(\tau + m\,\Delta\tau) + \sum_{-m+1}^{m-1}\delta(\tau - r\,\Delta\tau) + \tfrac{1}{2}\delta(\tau - m\,\Delta\tau)\right]$$

$$(10\text{--}36)$$

is a *finite Dirac comb*. Hence

$$\text{ave } \{V_s\} = Q_0(f;\Delta\tau) * P(f) \qquad f = \frac{s}{2m\,\Delta\tau},$$

where

$$Q_0(f;\Delta\tau) = \mathfrak{F}[\nabla_m(\tau;\Delta\tau)]. \qquad (10\text{--}37)$$

It is readily shown that

$$Q_0(f;\Delta\tau) = \Delta\tau\cot\frac{\omega\,\Delta\tau}{2}\sin m\omega\,\Delta\tau \qquad (10\text{--}38)$$

(see BT p. 71), but this formula is not so informative as the one which is derived as follows. Noting that

$$\nabla_m(\tau;\Delta\tau) = D_0(\tau)\nabla(\tau;\Delta\tau), \qquad (10\text{--}39)$$

where

$$\begin{aligned} D_0(\tau) &= 1 && \text{for } |\tau| < T_m, \quad T_m = m\,\Delta\tau, \\ &= \tfrac{1}{2} && \text{for } |\tau| - T_m, \\ &= 0 && \text{for } |\tau| > T_m, \end{aligned}$$

and

$$\nabla(\tau;\Delta\tau) = \Delta\tau\sum_{-\infty}^{\infty}\delta(\tau - r\,\Delta\tau) \qquad (10\text{--}40)$$

is an *infinite Dirac comb*, we have

$$Q_0(f;\Delta\tau) = Q_0(f) * A\left(f;\frac{1}{\Delta\tau}\right), \qquad (10\text{--}41)$$

where

$$A\left(f;\frac{1}{\Delta\tau}\right) = \mathfrak{F}[\nabla(\tau;\Delta\tau)]$$

$$= \sum_{-\infty}^{\infty}\delta\left(f - \frac{r}{\Delta\tau}\right) \qquad (10\text{--}42)$$

is also an "infinite Dirac comb" (see BT p. 71). Thus, upon performing the convolution, we get

$$Q_0(f;\Delta\tau) = \sum_{-\infty}^{\infty}Q_0\left(f - \frac{r}{\Delta\tau}\right). \qquad (10\text{--}43)$$

Disregarding the last step, however, we have

$$\text{ave } \{V_s\} = Q_0(f) * A\left(f; \frac{1}{\Delta\tau}\right) * P(f) \qquad \left(f = \frac{s}{2m \, \Delta\tau}\right). \qquad (10\text{-}44)$$

Finally, if, for example, the refined spectral density estimates are obtained by hamming the raw estimates, then

$$\text{ave } \{U_s\} = \nabla_{\text{hm}}(f) * Q_0(f) * A\left(f; \frac{1}{\Delta\tau}\right) * P(f) \qquad \left(f = \frac{s}{2m \, \Delta\tau}\right), \qquad (10\text{-}45)$$

where, as before,

$$\nabla_{\text{hm}}(f) = 0.54\delta(f) + 0.23\delta\left(f + \frac{1}{2T_m}\right) + 0.23\delta\left(f - \frac{1}{2T_m}\right) \qquad (T_m = m \, \Delta\tau).$$
$$(10\text{-}46)$$

Since multiple convolutions are commutative as well as associative, this result may be interpreted in a variety of ways, of which we will examine three. (The first is not important.)

1. Since

$$\nabla_{\text{hm}}(f) * Q_0(f) = Q_3(f)$$

and

$$Q_3(f) * P(f) = \text{ave } \{P_3(f)\},$$

where $P_3(f)$ is the power spectrum estimate by the "hypothetical indirect method" with continuous-time data, using the $Q_3(f)$ spectral window, we have

$$\text{ave } \{U_s\} = A\left(f; \frac{1}{\Delta\tau}\right) * \text{ave } \{P_3(f)\}, \qquad f = \frac{s}{2m \, \Delta\tau}.$$

2. We also have

$$\text{ave } \{U_s\} = Q_3(f) * P_a(f), \qquad f = \frac{s}{2m \, \Delta\tau},$$

where

$$P_a(f) = A\left(f; \frac{1}{\Delta\tau}\right) * P(f).$$

Here, $P_a(f)$ is a periodic function of f, symmetrical about every integral multiple of $1/(2 \, \Delta\tau)$. It is the *aliased* version of $P(f)$. It may be regarded as the result of simultaneous amplitude modulation of carrier frequencies located at every integral multiple of $1/\Delta\tau$. This point of view shows the importance of taking $\Delta\tau$ sufficiently small in order to avoid the situation shown in Fig. 10.9 (*overlapping side bands* is equivalent to *aliasing*).

The part of $P_a(f)$ in the range $-1/(2 \, \Delta\tau) < f < 1/(2 \, \Delta\tau)$ is called the *principal part*, denoted by $P_A(f)$. The relation of $P_A(f)$ to $P(f)$ may be regarded as a *folding* of $P(f)$ at every integral multiple of $1/(2 \, \Delta\tau)$. Hence, $1/(2 \, \Delta\tau)$ is called the *folding frequency*.

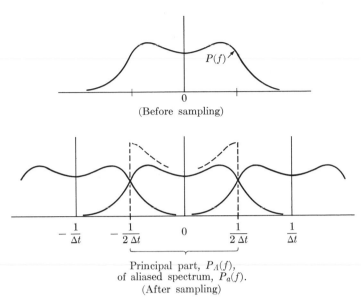

(Before sampling)

Principal part, $P_A(f)$,
of aliased spectrum, $P_a(f)$.
(After sampling)

FIG. 10.9.　Aliasing, or overlapping sidebands, due to sampling at too slow rate.

3. We also have

$$\text{ave}\ \{U_s\} = Q_{3A}(f) * P(f), \qquad f = \frac{s}{2m\,\Delta\tau},$$

where

$$Q_{3A}(f) = A\left(f, \frac{1}{\Delta\tau}\right) * Q_3(f).$$

Here, $Q_{3A}(f)$ is a periodic function of f, symmetrical about every integral multiple of $1/(2\,\Delta\tau)$. It is the aliased version of $Q_3(f)$. This point of view also shows the importance of taking $\Delta\tau$ sufficiently small so that only the principal part of $Q_{3A}(f)$ is effective.

Aliased versions of $Q_0(f)$, $Q_2(f)$, and $Q_3(f)$ for $m = 12$ are shown in Figs. 10.10, 10.11, and 10.12, respectively. They are symmetrical about every integral multiple of $1/(2\,\Delta\tau)$, but are hardly distinguishable from the unaliased spectral windows in the principal range $|f| \leq 1/(2\,\Delta\tau)$.

As in the continuous-time case, we may write

$$\text{ave}\ \{U_s\} = \frac{1}{2}\int H_{iA}\left(f; \frac{s}{2m\,\Delta\tau}\right) P(f)\,df,$$

where

$$H_{iA}(f;f_1) = Q_{iA}(f + f_1) + Q_{iA}(f - f_1).$$

10.9 Variability—degrees of freedom (BT pp. 37–39, 124–125). The basic relation of cov $\{U_r, U_s\}$ to the true power spectrum $P(f)$ is essentially the same as for cov $\{P_i(f_1), P_j(f_2)\}$. Details will be found in BT p. 125. It follows that if the refined spectral density estimates are obtained by either hanning or

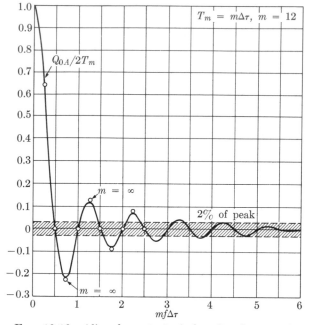

FIG. 10.10. Aliased spectral window Q_{0A} for $m = 12$.

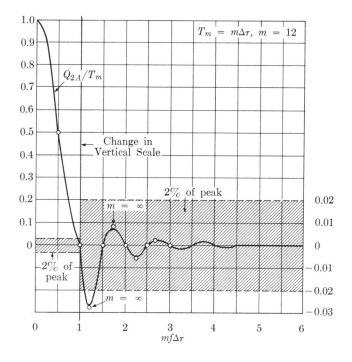

FIG. 10.11. Aliased spectral window Q_{2A} for $m = 12$.

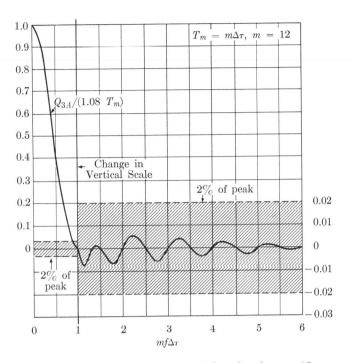

Fig. 10.12. Aliased spectral window Q_{3A} for $m = 12$.

hamming the raw estimates (no further refinement), then the stability of each refined estimate is approximately that of a chi-square on k degrees of freedom, where, by Eq. (10–35),

$$k = 2 \left(\frac{n \, \Delta t}{m \, \Delta \tau} - \frac{1}{3} \right)$$

$$= 2 \left(\frac{n}{hm} - \frac{1}{3} \right), \quad f = \frac{s}{2m \, \Delta \tau}, \quad s = 1, 2, \ldots, (m-1), \qquad (10\text{–}47)$$

(half as much at $f = 0$, and at $f = 1/2 \, \Delta \tau$).

The correction term $-\frac{2}{3}$ is usually insignificant, but it does show that a few long pieces are slightly better than many short pieces with the same total duration and for the same resolving power. Thus, for 15 pieces with $n \, \Delta t = 100$, and $m \, \Delta \tau = 10$, we get $k = 290$, while for 3 pieces with $n \, \Delta t = 500$ and $m \, \Delta \tau = 10$, we get $k = 298$.

It should be noted also that, as discussed in BT pp. 33, 44, there is really no point in taking $\Delta \tau$ a multiple of Δt or, more accurately, to having chosen Δt so small that we can afford to take $\Delta \tau$ a multiple of Δt. If we can afford to take a folding frequency of $1/(2 \, \Delta \tau)$, then we need not have taken Δt any smaller than $\Delta \tau$. (However, see the discussion under "Prefiltering and prewhitening," below.)

10.10 Confidence limits. Referring to the cumulative probability distribution of a chi-square on 4 degrees of freedom shown in Fig. 10.7, we see that there is a 5% probability that a sample value will fall below 0.7 and a 5% probability that the sample value will fall above 9.5. Thus, there is a probability of 90% that the ratio of the sample value to the average value (namely, 4) will fall between $0.7/4 = 0.175$ and $9.5/4 = 2.375$. However, as far at least as the measurement of power spectra is concerned, the practical situation is that we have an estimate of the average value of an *unknown multiple* of a chi-square on a known (approximate) number of degrees of freedom. On 4 degrees of freedom, there is a probability of 90% that the ratio of the unknown average value to the estimate is between $4/9.5 = 0.421$ and $4/0.7 = 5.71$. This pair of ratios is quite different from the first pair, but since the two pairs are reciprocally related, they would be the same, except for signs, if the ratios were expressed in logarithmic units. It is convenient here to say that the 90% confidence limits for a chi-square (or multiple of a chi-square) on 4 degrees of freedom are $10 \log_{10}(4/9.5) = -3.76$ db, and $10 \log_{10}(4/0.7) = 7.57$ db. It is from this point of view that the curves in Fig. 10.13 were drawn. These curves are closely approximated by

$$10.0 \left(\frac{2}{3k - 1} \pm \frac{1}{\sqrt{k - 1}} \right) \text{db} \qquad \text{for } k \geq 3. \qquad (10\text{--}48)$$

Similarly, 80% confidence limits are closely approximated by

$$7.8 \left(\frac{2}{3k - 1} \pm \frac{1}{\sqrt{k - 1}} \right) \text{db}. \qquad (10\text{--}49)$$

For 98% confidence limits, the leading factor in these expressions is 14.3, and for 96% confidence limits, it is 12.6.

10.11 Independence of estimates—resolution. The raw spectral density estimates, V_s, located at integral multiples of $1/(2m \, \Delta\tau)$, are usually very nearly uncorrelated. In fact, if the true spectrum were flat up to $1/(2 \, \Delta\tau)$, zero beyond (so-called bandlimited white noise), then cov $\{V_r, V_s\} = 0$ if $r \neq s$, because

$$\int \frac{\sin (m\omega \, \Delta\tau - \pi r)}{m\omega \, \Delta\tau - \pi r} \frac{\sin (m\omega \, \Delta\tau - \pi s)}{m\omega \, \Delta\tau - \pi s} \, df = \frac{1}{2m \, \Delta\tau} \frac{\sin \pi(r - s)}{\pi(r - s)}.$$

If the refined spectral density estimates, U_s, are obtained by hamming the raw estimates, then

$$U_i = 0.23 \, V_{i-1} + 0.54 \, V_i + 0.23 \, V_{i+1}$$

$$U_{i+1} = 0.23 \, V_i + 0.54 \, V_{i+1} + 0.23 \, V_{i+2}.$$

Hence, cov $\{U_i, U_{i+1}\} = 0.2484$ var $\{V_i\}$. Since var $\{U_i\} = 0.3974$ var $\{V_i\}$, the correlation coefficient between U_i and U_{i+1} is 0.625. In the same way, we find that the correlation coefficient between U_i and U_{i+2} is 0.133. These results should be compared with $\rho(0.25)$ and $\rho(0.5)$ in Table 1 above.

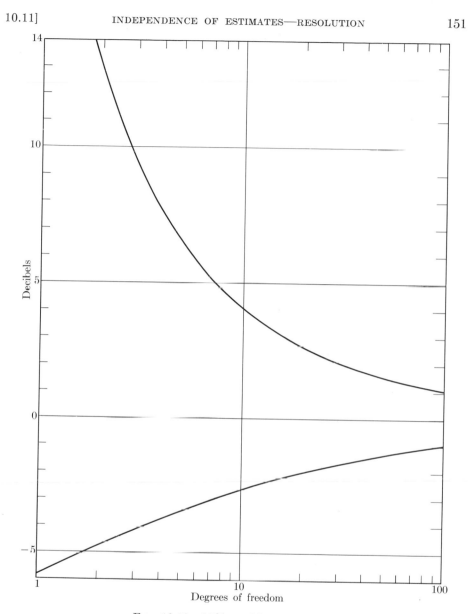

Decibels

Degrees of freedom

FIG. 10.13.　90% confidence limits.

For practical purposes we may regard hanned or hammed spectral density estimates separated by at least two units of $1/(2m\,\Delta\tau)$ to be *independent* or *resolved* (BT p. 147). In accordance with the discussion of ordinary sampling theory, therefore, the stability of the *sum* of the refined spectral density estimates should be approximately that of a chi-square on K degrees of freedom, where

$$K = k\,\frac{(\tfrac{1}{2}U_0 + U_2 + U_4 + \cdots + \tfrac{1}{2}U_m)^2}{\tfrac{1}{2}U_0^2 + U_2^2 + U_4^2 + \cdots + \tfrac{1}{2}U_m^2}\,. \qquad (10\text{-}50)$$

This happens to give exactly what we would expect $(K = n)$ for white noise, bandlimited at $1/(2\,\Delta\tau)$, if we take $k = 2n/m$ without the correction term.

10.12 Removal of trends (BT pp. 47–49, 139–146). We have been assuming, and will continue to assume, that the ensemble average, ave $\{X(t)\}$, is identically zero for any value of t. It does not necessarily follow from this assumption that the mean of the data should be zero. If we could be certain that the data did not include a spurious zero-point bias large enough to substantially affect the power density estimates near zero frequency, we would not be concerned over the fact that the mean of the data is not zero. However, such certainty is rarely attainable.

A spurious zero-point bias is essentially a concentration of a finite amount of power (of infinite density, as in a delta function) at zero frequency. This power may be so small, compared with the total power in the spectrum of the random process under measurement that its presence may not be detectable except by computation. However, if the spectral density in the neighborhood of zero frequency is very low, spectral density estimates in this neighborhood may be substantially affected by it.

Hence, we will usually want to be protected from the effects of zero-point bias. We may also want to be protected against a constant rate of change (that is, drift) of zero-point bias. These objectives may be secured at either of two points in the computational procedure, either before computing mean lagged products or immediately after. Let us consider the latter choice.

We require numbers E_r, which are to be subtracted from the mean lagged products C_r in order to reduce or eliminate the effects of zero-point bias and drift, before computing raw spectral density estimates. Let us assume that zero-point bias and drift are expressed by

$$\hat{X}_i = \alpha + \beta\,\Delta t\left(i - \frac{n}{2}\right), \qquad i = 0, 1, 2, \ldots, n.$$

Taking $\Delta\tau = \Delta t$, these will add

$$E_r = \alpha^2 + \beta^2\,\frac{(n\,\Delta t)^2}{12}\,K_r \tag{10–51}$$

to the true mean lagged products, where

$$K_r = 1 + \frac{2}{n} - 2\left(1 + \frac{1}{n}\right)\frac{r}{n} - \frac{2r^2}{n^2}.$$

For large n, and for r ranging up to $n/10$, we may simplify matters by arbitrarily taking $K_r = 1$, or, a little better,

$$K_r = 1 - \frac{m}{n}. \tag{10–52}$$

The next question (since α and β are not known) is, "What should we use for α and β?" As far as α is concerned, the obvious and simplest answer is the mean of the actual data,

$$\alpha = \frac{1}{n+1} \sum_{i=0}^{n} X_i. \tag{10-53}$$

As far as β is concerned, several possibilities are considered in BT pp. 142–145. The choice is not critical. For further analysis here, let us take

$$\beta = \frac{\sum_{n-n_1}^{n} X_i - \sum_{0}^{n_1} X_i}{(n - n_1)(n_1 + 1)\,\Delta t}, \tag{10-54}$$

where n_1 is the nearest integer to $(n - 2)/3$. This formula simply says: subtract the mean of approximately the first third of the series from the mean of approximately the last third of the series, and divide by the difference between the centroids of the two groups. The basis for this particular way of grouping the data for an estimate of the slope is discussed in Section 8.2, and in Jeffreys (1948) p. 193.

These choices for α and β complete the specification of E_r, which in this case is actually independent of r. In the procedure for computing the raw spectral density estimates, V_s, we should now use $C_r - E_r$ in place of C_r.

The final question is, "What does this procedure for the removal of trends give in the way of a spectral window before hanning or hamming?" To answer this question conveniently, let us derive and examine the result of the analogous procedure in the hypothetical continuous-time case. Here, the raw spectral estimate would be

$$P_0(f) = \mathfrak{F}\{D_0(\tau)[C_{00}(\tau) - A_0 - A_1]\},$$

where

$$A_0 = \left[\frac{1}{T_n} \int_{-T_n/2}^{T_n/2} X(t)\,dt\right]$$

$$A_1 = \frac{3}{16}\left(1 - \frac{T_m}{T_n}\right)\left[\frac{3}{T_n}\int_{T_n/6}^{T_n/2} X(t)\,dt - \frac{3}{T_n}\int_{-T_n/2}^{-T_n/6} X(t)\,dt\right]^2.$$

Note that while A_0 and A_1 are fixed for any single piece of $X(t)$, they are random variables in the ensemble of such pieces of the same length T_n. In fact, writing

$$A_0 = \frac{1}{T_n^2} \iint B(t_1)B(t_2)X(t_1)X(t_2)\,dt_1\,dt_2,$$

where

$$B(t) = 1 \qquad \text{for } |t| < \frac{T_n}{2},$$

$$= 0 \qquad \text{for } |t| > \frac{T_n}{2},$$

it is a simple matter to derive

$$\text{ave}\ \{A_0\} = \int\left[\frac{\sin(\omega T_n/2)}{(\omega T_n/2)}\right]^2 P(f)\,df.$$

Similarly, we find that

$$\text{ave } \{A_1\} = 3\left(1 - \frac{T_m}{T_n}\right)\int\left[\frac{\sin\,(\omega T_n/3)}{(\omega T_n/3)}\right]^2 [\sin\,(\omega T_n/6)]^2 P(f)\ df.$$

Thus, we get

$$\text{ave } \{P_0(f_1)\} = \int [Q_0(f_1 - f) - Q_0(f_1)\hat{Q}(f)]P(f)\ df, \qquad (10\text{--}55)$$

where

$$\hat{Q}(f) = \left[\frac{\sin\,(\omega T_n/2)}{(\omega T_n/2)}\right]^2 + 3\left(1 - \frac{T_m}{T_n}\right)\left[\frac{\sin\,(\omega T_n/3)}{(\omega T_n/3)}\right]^2 [\sin\,(\omega T_n/6)]^2. \quad (10\text{--}56)$$

As we should expect,

$$[Q_0(f_1 - f) - Q_0(f_1)\hat{Q}(f)]_{f=0} = 0 \qquad \text{for any } f_1,$$

so that ave $\{P_0(f_1)\}$ is not affected by any $\delta(f)$ component in $P(f)$, spurious or legitimate. In other respects, the relation of ave $\{P_0(f_1)\}$ to $P(f)$ may perhaps be understood better from the following observations.

1. $Q_0(f_1 - f)$ is a spectral window of base-width $1/T_m$ centered at $f = f_1$.

2. $\hat{Q}(f)$ is a spectral window of base-width $3/T_n$, permanently centered at $f = 0$.

3. $Q_0(f_1)$ is not a spectral window, but simply a multiplicative factor whose value depends on f_1.

The power which passes through the window $\hat{Q}(f)$ comes essentially only from that part of $P(f)$ which lies in the range $-3/(2T_n) < f < 3/(2T_n)$, or $1\frac{1}{2}$ elementary bands each side of $f = 0$. On the other hand, the window $Q_0(f_1 - f)$ is typically 10 elementary bands wide, and, after hanning or hamming, the limit of resolution is about 10 elementary bandwidths. Thus, we see that this method of removing trends will have little or no effect on the spectral density estimates down to $f_1 = 1/(2T_m)$.

10.13 Prefiltering and prewhitening (BT pp. 28–30, 39–42, 50–52, 116–117).

Consider the situation shown in Fig. 10.14. If sampling is done at a rate of not much more than $2f_c$ readings per second, all of the background noise spectrum will be folded into the frequency range of the spectrum to be measured. If the background noise is not largely due to reading errors, excessive folding may be avoided either (a) by analog filtering before sampling or (b) by sampling at a suitably higher rate, filtering numerically, and subsampling (*decimation*). However, if the background noise is largely due to reading errors plan (b) might be more effective than plan (a).

In the computation of spectral density estimates, the fact that spectral windows are symmetrical and have side lobes may give rise to large errors in the estimates at frequencies where the slope of the spectrum is very large. A method of effectively desymmetrizing the spectral windows and reducing the size of the side lobes on one side relative to the size of the side lobes on the other side of the

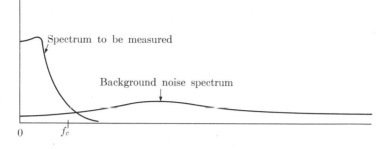

FIG. 10.14. A situation requiring analog prefiltering (or high-rate sampling and numerical prefiltering) before low-rate sampling (or subsampling).

main lobe is actually to pass the data through a filter which will make the power spectrum somewhat flatter (that is, nearer to white noise) before computing spectral density estimates with standard spectral windows. The estimates obtained in this way must of course be corrected for prewhitening.

10.14 Numerical filtering (BT pp. 42–43, 125–129). The topics beyond this point depend on an understanding of what is meant by the power transfer function of a *moving linear combination* scheme in which a time series $\{v_k\}$ is generated from a time series $\{u_k\}$ in accordance with the equation

$$v_k = A_0 u_k + A_1 u_{k-1} + \cdots + A_r u_{k-r} - B_1 v_{k-1} - B_2 v_{k-2} - \cdots - B_s v_{k-s}.$$
$$(10\text{--}57)$$

The term *moving linear combination* is usually applied, as in BT, only when there are no B coefficients, and the term *autoregressive combination* when there are no A coefficients other than A_0. Here, we call such a moving linear combination *nonrecursive* when there are no B coefficients, *recursive* when there is at least one B coefficient.

Let us imagine (what is frequently true) that the time series $\{u_k\}$ is obtained by sampling a continuous-time function $u(t)$ and that the computation is made by a digital computer, as shown in Fig. 10.15 (a). It will be readily seen that the time series $\{v_k\}$ may also be obtained by sampling the continuous-time function $v(t)$ generated from $u(t)$ by an *analog* computer (of *transversal filter* type) in accordance with the equation

$$v(t) = A_0 u(t) + A_1 u(t - \Delta t) + \cdots + A_r u(t - r\,\Delta t) - B_1 v(t - \Delta t)$$
$$- B_2 v(t - 2\,\Delta t) - \cdots - B_s v(t - s\,\Delta t), \qquad (10\text{--}58)$$

as shown in Fig. 10.15(b). The transfer function of the analog computer is

$$Y(i\omega) = \frac{A_0 + A_1 q + A_2 q^2 + \cdots + A_r q^r}{1 + B_1 q + B_2 q^2 + \cdots + B_s q^s}, \qquad (10\text{--}59)$$

where

$$q = e^{-i\omega\,\Delta t}. \qquad (10\text{--}60)$$

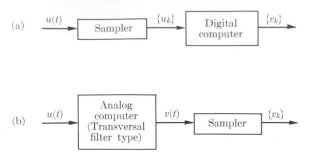

FIG. 10.15. Basic equivalence defining transfer function of a discrete-data filter.

This is taken to be the transfer function of the digital computer (assuming no roundoff, and no computing time) or the transfer function of the moving linear combination scheme. The power transfer function $|Y(i\omega)|^2$ is a rational function of $\cos \omega \, \Delta t$, and is, therefore, symmetrical about every integral multiple of $1/(2 \, \Delta t)$ cycles/sec.

The following examples are apropos the topics discussed later (Sections 10.17 and on). A very simple high-pass filtration is obtained from

$$v_k = \tfrac{1}{2}(u_k - u_{k-1}).\tag{10-61}$$

Then,

$$Y(i\omega) = \tfrac{1}{2}(1 - e^{-i\omega\Delta t}),$$

whence

$$|Y(i\omega)|^2 = \tfrac{1}{2}(1 - \cos \omega \, \Delta t).\tag{10-62}$$

The power transfer function is shown by the solid curve in Fig. 10.16.

The complementary low-pass filtration is obtained from

$$v_k = \tfrac{1}{2}(u_k + u_{k-1}).\tag{10-63}$$

Then,

$$|Y(i\omega)|^2 = \tfrac{1}{2}(1 + \cos \omega \, \Delta t).\tag{10-64}$$

The power transfer function is shown by the broken curve in Fig. 10.16.

A very useful generalization of the preceding method of low-pass filtration is that of *simple averaging,*

$$v_k = \frac{1}{n} (u_k + u_{k-1} + \cdots + u_{k-n+1}).\tag{10-65}$$

The corresponding transfer function is

$$Y(i\omega) = \frac{\sin (\omega n \, \Delta t/2)}{n \sin (\omega \, \Delta t/2)} e^{-i\omega(n-1)\Delta t/2},$$

and the power transfer function is

$$|Y(i\omega)|^2 = \left[\frac{\sin (\omega n \, \Delta t/2)}{n \sin (\omega \, \Delta t/2)}\right]^2.\tag{10-66}$$

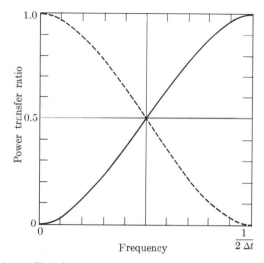

1.0

Power transfer ratio

0.5

0

0

Frequency

$\dfrac{1}{2\,\Delta t}$

FIG. 10.16. Simple complementary power transfer functions.

Cascading simple averagings is a very effective way of getting a single averaging with nonuniform weighting with only one multiplication or division. For example, a cascade of simple averagings by twos, by threes, and by fours in any order is equivalent to a single averaging with relative weights 1, 3, 5, 6, 5, 3, 1. A cascade of three simple averagings by threes is equivalent to a single averaging with relative weights 1, 3, 6, 7, 6, 3, 1 (see Chapter 8).

A disadvantage of simple averaging by n's is the fact that the zeros of the transfer function are located at all integral multiples of $1/(n\,\Delta t)$ up to the folding frequency. If we wanted a transfer function in which the first zero is located at 2/9 of the folding frequency, we would have to accept zeros at 4/9, 2/3, and 8/9 of the folding frequency. Clearly, it might be useful to have a way of getting a transfer function with a single zero located anywhere below the folding frequency. Such a way is offered by

$$v_k = A_0 u_k + A_1 u_{k-1} + A_2 u_{k-2}, \qquad (10\text{–}67)$$

where

$$A_0 = A_2 = \frac{1}{2(1 - \cos \omega_0\,\Delta t)}, \qquad A_1 = 1 - 2A_0. \qquad (10\text{–}68)$$

The corresponding power transfer function is

$$|Y(i\omega)|^2 = \left\{1 - \left[\frac{\sin(\omega\,\Delta t/2)}{\sin(\omega_0\,\Delta t/2)}\right]^2\right\}^2. \qquad (10\text{–}69)$$

This has its own disadvantage, however, inasmuch as the transfer loss may become too low in the range $f_0 < f < 1/(2\,\Delta t)$. In fact, if $f_0 < 1/(4\,\Delta t)$, then

$|Y(i\omega)|^2 > 1$ for f in the range

$$\frac{1}{\pi \, \Delta t} \sin^{-1} \left(\sqrt{2} \sin \frac{\omega_0 \, \Delta t}{2} \right) < f \leq \frac{1}{2 \, \Delta t}.$$

The lower limit of this range varies from $\sqrt{2} f_0$ to $2 f_0$ as f_0 is increased from zero to $1/(4 \, \Delta t)$. To maintain a minimum transfer loss beyond f_0 we may have to resort to cascading. Whether or not this method has any advantage over simple averagings will, therefore, depend upon circumstances.

10.15 A general method of designing numerical filters and equalizers of nonrecursive type.† A power transfer function of the form

$$|Y(i\omega)|^2 = B_0 + B_1 \cos \omega \, \Delta t + \cdots + B_m \cos m\omega \, \Delta t \qquad (10\text{–}70)$$

is easily fitted approximately to any desired shape in the range $0 \leq \omega \leq \pi/\Delta t$. To determine a corresponding transfer function

$$Y(i\omega) = A_0 + A_1 q + \cdots + A_m q^m, \qquad (10\text{–}71)$$

where $q = e^{-i\omega \, \Delta t}$, we proceed as follows.

1. Express the power transfer function as a polynomial in (powers of) $\cos \omega \, \Delta t$.

2. Substitute $\cos \omega \, \Delta t = (1 + z^2)/(1 - z^2)$, and rationalize.

3. Evaluate the roots, and express in the form

$$|Y|^2 = \frac{F(z)F(-z)}{(1 - z^2)^m},$$

where $F(z)$ is a polynomial of degree m, with real coefficients. Of the various ways in which the roots may be assigned either to $F(z)$ or to $F(-z)$, the one which yields the minimum-phase $Y(i\omega)$ is that in which $F(z)$ has no root in $\text{Re}[z] > 0$. (For the significance and importance of minimum phase, see Bode, 1945.)

4. In any case,

$$Y(i\omega) = \left(\frac{1 + q}{2} \right)^m F \left(\frac{1 - q}{1 + q} \right). \qquad (10\text{–}72)$$

An easier but less efficient method is based on the observation that if the A's in $Y(i\omega)$ are restricted by $A_r = A_{m-r}$, then

$$Y(i\omega) = G(\omega) e^{-i\omega m \Delta t/2}, \qquad (10\text{–}73)$$

---

† An equalizer is essentially a filter, but its function is not so much the suppression of frequency components outside of the signal band as it is to modify the transmission characteristics within the signal band. It may be used to preemphasize some parts of the signal band (as in the recording of music), as well as to flatten the overall transmission in the signal band (as in the reproduction of recorded music).

where, if m is even and equal to $2n$,

$$G(\omega) = A_n + 2A_{n-1} \cos \omega \, \Delta t + \cdots + 2A_0 \cos n\omega \, \Delta t, \qquad (10\text{–}74)$$

while, if m is odd and equal to $2n + 1$,

$$G(\omega) = 2A_n \cos \frac{\omega \, \Delta t}{2} + 2A_{n-1} \cos \frac{3\omega \, \Delta t}{2} + \cdots + 2A_0 \cos \frac{m\omega \, \Delta t}{2}. \qquad (10\text{–}75)$$

It should be noted that in fitting $G(\omega)$ approximately to the desired shape of $\pm |Y(i\omega)|$ we are free to shift from one branch to the other wherever the desired shape goes through zero. It should be noted also that the phase in Eq. (10–73) is linear in frequency.

10.16 Numerical filters and equalizers of recursive type. Transfer functions which are rational functions of $q = e^{-i\omega \Delta t}$ may be derived from transfer functions which are rational functions of $i\Omega$, by means of the *frequency transformation*

$$\Omega = \frac{2}{\Delta t} \tan \frac{\omega \, \Delta t}{2},$$

or, equivalently,

$$i\Omega = \frac{2}{\Delta t} \frac{1 - q}{1 + q} \qquad \text{(see Chapter 5)}.$$

In particular, if the denominator of the prototype transfer function is of the form

$$\left(1 + \frac{i\Omega \, \Delta t}{2}\right)^n,$$

the derived transfer function will be simply a polynomial in q.

An advantage of the frequency transformation method is the fact that if the shape of the transfer function is known in terms of Ω, it need not be computed in terms of ω. In particular, equal-ripple (so-called Tchebycheff) transfer functions in terms of Ω transform into equal-ripple transfer functions in terms of ω. Similarly, maximally-flat (so-called Butterworth) transfer functions in terms of Ω, transform into maximally-flat transfer functions in terms of ω.

A prototype transfer function which is often useful is

$$Y(i\Omega) = \frac{1 + 2\beta(i\Omega \, \Delta t/2) + \alpha^2 (i\Omega \, \Delta t/2)^2}{(1 + i\Omega \, \Delta t/2)^2}.$$

The prototype power transfer function is

$$|Y|^2 = \frac{1 - 2(\alpha^2 - 2\beta^2)h + \alpha^4 h^2}{(1 + h)^2}, \qquad h = \left(\frac{\Omega \, \Delta t}{2}\right)^2.$$

Then,

$$|Y|^2 \approx 1 - 2(1 + \alpha^2 - 2\beta^2)h, \qquad h \to 0,$$

$$|Y|^2 \approx \alpha^4 - \frac{2(\alpha^2 + \alpha^4 - 2\beta^2)}{h}, \qquad h \to \infty, \qquad \left(f \to \frac{1}{2 \, \Delta t}\right),$$

$|Y|^2 = 1$ at $h = 0$, and under appropriate conditions at

$$h_1 = \frac{2(1 + \alpha^2 - 2\beta^2)}{\alpha^4 - 1},$$

$$\frac{d}{dh}|Y|^2 = \frac{2}{(1 + h)^3}[-(1 + \alpha^2 - 2\beta^2) + (\alpha^2 + \alpha^4 - 2\beta^2)h].$$

Thus, for example, if $\alpha < 1$, and $2\beta^2 < \alpha^2(1 + \alpha^2)$, then $|Y|^2$ must drop from 1 at $h = 0$, to a minimum at

$$h_m = \frac{1 + \alpha^2 - 2\beta^2}{\alpha^2 + \alpha^4 - 2\beta^2},$$

and rise to α^4 as $h \to \infty$. The value of h_m is least when $\beta = 0$. If $\beta = 0$, then $h_m = 1/\alpha^2$ and $|Y|^2 = 0$ at $h = h_m$.

If $\alpha = 1$, then $h_m = 1$. The power transfer function is maximum at $h = 1$ if $|\beta| > 1$; minimum if $|\beta| < 1$.

10.17 Pilot estimation (BT pp. 45–47, 135–136). The *add-and-subtract* method of pilot estimation is described and illustrated in BT pp. 45–47. This method is clearly based on the first two examples considered under "Numerical Filtering" (Section 10.14), except that the differences and sums by twos (denoted by δ and σ, respectively, in BT) are not halved. Here, we will show how the results are related to the mean spectral density estimates in consecutive octaves coming down from the folding frequency.

For generality, let 2^r be the number of X_q's. To get the mean spectral density estimate for the first octave, the sum of the $(\delta X_q)^2$ should be divided by 2^2 to normalize the filtering; then divided by 2^{r-1}, the number of terms in the column; and then divided by $1/(4\,\Delta t)$, the width of the octave: a net division by $2^{r-1}/\Delta t$. To get the mean spectral density estimate for the second octave, the sum of the $(\delta\sigma X_q)^2$ should be divided by 2^4, to normalize the two filterings; then divided by 2^{r-2}, the number of terms in the column; and then divided by $1/(8\,\Delta t)$, the width of the octave: a net division by $2^{r-1}/\Delta t$, as before. Clearly, the same net divisor should be applied to the sum of any $(\delta\sigma^{i-1}X_q)^2$ to get the mean spectral density estimate for the ith octave, where $i = 1, 2, \ldots, r$, as well as to $(\sigma^r X_q)^2$ to get the mean spectral density estimate for the remaining frequency range below the rth octave.

The procedure need not be carried out to $(\sigma^r X_q)^2$ as illustrated in BT p. 46. We may stop with $(\delta\sigma^{j-1}X_q)^2$ for the jth octave and then compute $(\sigma^j X_q)^2$ for the remaining frequency range below the jth octave, where $j < r$.

A modification of the add-and-subtract method of pilot estimation is described in BT pp. 135–136 and illustrated in BT pp. 154–155. The object of this modification is to get more stability of the spectral density estimates. The purpose of the gaps in a typical column of $S^i X$ terms in Table VI in BT, p. 136 and in Table IX in BT, pp. 154–155 is to serve as a reminder to omit the difference between terms separated by a gap in computing the corresponding column of $DS^i X$ terms.

Under the simple add-and-subtract procedure, the mean spectral density estimate for the ith octave will have approximately the stability of a chi-square on 2^{r-i} degrees of freedom, and the mean spectral density estimate for the remaining frequency range below the jth octave will have approximately the stability of a chi-square on 2^{r-j} degrees of freedom. Thus, it may not be desirable to go beyond $j = r - 4$.

The estimate of the total power in the spectrum,

$$P_T = \frac{P_1}{4\,\Delta t} + \frac{P_2}{8\,\Delta t} + \cdots + \frac{P_j}{2^{j+1}\,\Delta t} + \frac{\hat{P}_j}{2^{j+1}\,\Delta t},$$

(where P_i is the mean spectral density for the ith octave and $\hat{P}_j$ is the mean spectral density for the remaining frequency range below the jth octave) will have approximately the stability of a chi-square on K degrees of freedom, where

$$K = 2^{r-j}\,\frac{(2^{j-1}P_1 + 2^{j-2}P_2 + \cdots + P_j + \hat{P}_j)^2}{2^{j-1}P_1^2 + 2^{j-2}P_2^2 + \cdots + P_j^2 + \hat{P}_j^2}.$$

For bandlimited white noise, cutting off at $1/(2\,\Delta t)$, all of the P_i's including $\hat{P}_j$ are equal, and therefore $K = 2^r$ as it should be. If cutoff is at $1/(4\,\Delta t)$ so that $P_1 = 0$, then $K = 2^{r-1}$, again as it should be.

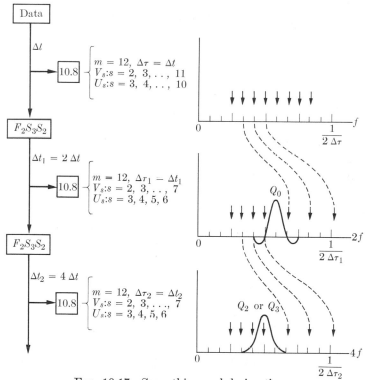

FIG. 10.17. Smoothing and decimation.

10.18 Smoothing and decimation (BT pp. 44–45, 129–135, 137–139). The term *smoothing* is here used in the sense of *low-pass numerical filtering*, usually by cascaded simple averagings. The operation of simple averaging by α's is denoted by S_α. The term *decimation* refers to the operation of casting out all but every βth term, say, of a time series. This operation is denoted by F_β.

A typical smoothing and decimation procedure is outlined in block schematic form in Fig. 10.17. The blocks marked 10.8 refer to a limited use of the procedure of power spectrum analysis described under Section 10.8. It should be noted that the sampling interval doubles at each application of F_2. The diagrams on the right-hand side show the position of the computed spectral density estimates on the frequency axis. In order to show how typical spectral windows fit the frequency scales, one of these diagrams shows the main lobe and two side lobes of the $Q_0(f)$ spectral window, and one diagram shows the main lobe of the $Q_2(f)$ or $Q_3(f)$ spectral window. The diagrams are connected by dashed curves to show corresponding frequencies.

The purpose of each S_3S_2 operation is to protect against aliasing due to folding by the subsequent F_2 operation. Table 2 gives the power transfer ratio, the power transfer loss in db, and the protection in db for the S_3S_2 operation. (The *protection* in db is the difference between the losses at points located symmetrically about the middle of the frequency range and therefore folded together by F_2.) It will be seen that the protection is better than 20 db (corresponding to a ratio of 100 to 1) from $f = 0$ to $\frac{3}{4}$ of the folding frequency of the next computational cycle.

TABLE 2

$24f\,\Delta t_i$	Ratio	Loss (db)	Protection (db)
0	1	0	∞
1	0.938	0.28	27.56
2	0.773	1.12	22.88
2.5	0.666	1.76	22.29
3	0.553	2.58	22.96
4	0.3333	4.77	∞
4.5	0.2388	6.22	21.04
5	0.1610	7.94	12.26
6	0.0556	12.55	0
7	0.00956	20.20	
7.5	0.001883	27.26	
8	0	∞	
9	0.002796	25.54	
9.5	0.003936	24.05	
10	0.003984	24.00	
11	0.001642	27.84	
12	0	∞	

10.19 Correction of estimates (BT pp. 53, 146–147). Spectral density estimates computed by the procedure described in Section 10.8 must, of course, be corrected for the effects of prefiltering and prewhitening, and those computed by the procedure described in Section 10.18 must be corrected also for the effects of smoothing and decimation.

$$F_3 F_2 = F_6$$

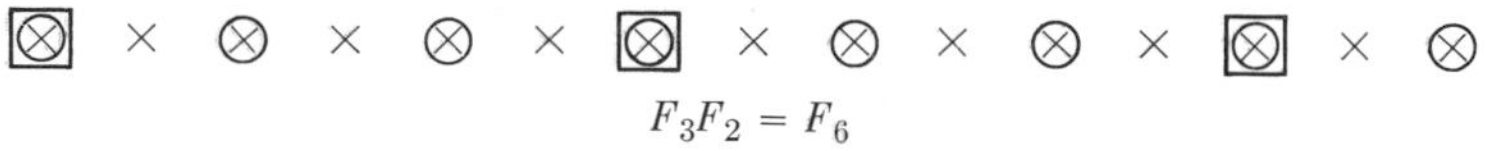

FIG. 10.18. Consecutive decimations.

The correction of a spectral density estimate for the effects of smoothing and decimation involves the addition of all of the losses incurred at that frequency in all of the preceding stages of filtering. For this purpose, we may formulate the transfer function for any sequence of simple averagings and decimations by following certain rules of manipulation. Following the convention of ordering operators from right to left, the rules are:

(a) $$F_\beta F_\alpha = F_\gamma, \quad \text{where } \gamma = \alpha\beta. \tag{10-76}$$

This is illustrated in Fig. 10.18 where the crosses represent the original time series, the circles represent the series after the operation F_2, and the squares represent the series after the operation $F_3 F_2$.

(b) $$S_\beta F_\alpha = F_\alpha S_\beta^{(\alpha)}, \tag{10-77}$$

where S_β is *simple averaging by β's*, defined by

$$v_k = \frac{1}{\beta}(u_k + u_{k-1} + u_{k-2} + \cdots + u_{k-\beta+1}),$$

and $S_\beta^{(\alpha)}$ is *simple averaging by β's at spacing of α units*, defined by

$$v_k = \frac{1}{\beta}(u_k + u_{k-\alpha} + u_{k-2\alpha} + \cdots + u_{k-\alpha(\beta-1)}).$$

Fig. 10.19 illustrates $S_2 F_3 = F_3 S_2^{(3)}$.

(c) $$S_\beta^{(\alpha)} S_\alpha = S_\alpha S_\beta^{(\alpha)} = S_\gamma, \quad \text{where } \gamma = \alpha\beta. \tag{10-78}$$

This rule follows from the fact that S_α corresponds to filtering with transfer function

$$Y(i\omega) = \left(\frac{\sin(\alpha\omega\,\Delta t/2)}{\alpha\sin(\omega\,\Delta t/2)}\right) e^{-i\omega(\alpha-1)\Delta t/2}, \tag{10-79}$$

while $S_\beta^{(\alpha)}$ corresponds to filtering with power transfer function

$$Y(i\omega) = \left(\frac{\sin(\alpha\beta\omega\,\Delta t/2)}{\beta\sin(\alpha\omega\,\Delta t/2)}\right) e^{-i\omega\alpha(\beta-1)\Delta t/2}. \tag{10-80}$$

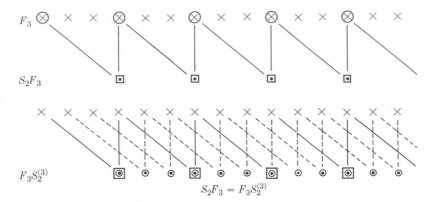

FIG. 10.19. Commutation of a decimation with a smoothing.

It should be noted that the power transfer ratio for $S_\beta^{(\alpha)}$ at $f = f_1$ has the same value as the power transfer ratio for S_β at $f = \alpha f_1$.

(d) $$S_\beta^{(\gamma)} F_\alpha = F_\alpha S_\beta^{(\lambda)}, \qquad \text{where } \lambda = \alpha\gamma. \qquad (10\text{--}81)$$

The justification for this rule is similar to that for rule (b).

These rules allow us to convert any sequence of S's and F's into a sequence of S's followed by only one F, thereby simplifying the problem of determining the corresponding transfer function. For example,

$$S_3 F_2 S_4 F_3 S_3 = F_6 S_3^{(6)} S_{12},$$

$$S_3 F_4 S_4 F_3 S_3 = F_{12} S_{36}.$$

Using Eqs. (10–79) and (10–80), the transfer function of a sequence of S's may be formulated. If this transfer function is denoted by $Y_S(f)$, where for convenience we now use frequency in cycles per second as the argument, then a single final decimation operation, say F_n, gives the transfer function

$$Y_{FS}(f) = \sum_{m=-n+1}^{m=n-1} Y_S\left(f + \frac{m}{n\,\Delta t}\right).$$

This transfer function, of course, does not need to be computed beyond the folding frequency $f = 1/(2n\,\Delta t)$.

REFERENCES

AKCASU, A. Z. (1961): "Measurement of Noise Power Spectra by Fourier Analysis." *J. Appl. Phys.*, **32** (1961) 565–568.

BA HLI, F. (1954): "A General Method for Time Domain Network Synthesis." *IRE Trans. on Circuit Theory*, **CT-1** (1954) 21–28.

BAKER, R. M. L. Jr., MAKEMSON, M. W. (1960): *An Introduction to Astrodynamics.* (Academic Press, 1960) pp. 142–145.

BARTLETT, M. S. (1955): *An Introduction to Stochastic Processes.* (Cambridge, 1955)

BENDAT, J. S. (1957a): "Optimum Filters for Independent Measurements of Two Related Perturbed Messages." *IRE Trans. on Circuit Theory*, **CT-4** (1957) 14–19.

BENDAT, J. S. (1958): *Principles and Applications of Random Noise Theory.* (Wiley, 1958)

BLACKMAN, R. B. (1944a): "*Design and Performance of Data-Smoothing Network.*" *OEMsr-262, Report*, Bell Telephone Laboratories, Incorporated, July 3, 1944.

BLACKMAN, R. B. (1944b): "A Position and Rate Smoothing Circuit for Ground-Controlled Bombing Computers." *OEMsr-262, Report*, Bell Telephone Laboratories, Incorporated, August 21, 1944.

BLACKMAN, R. B. (1944c): "A Two-Servo Circuit for Smoothing Present Position Coordinates and Rates in Antiaircraft Gun Directors." *Contract W-30-069-ORD-1448, Report*, Bell Telephone Laboratories, Incorporated, September 27, 1944.

BLACKMAN, R. B. (1960): "Smoothing and Prediction of Time Series by Cascaded Simple Averages." *1960 IRE Nat. Conv. Record*, Vol. 8, pt. 2, pp. 47–54; *IRE Trans. on Circuit Theory*, **CT-7,** Special Supplement (August, 1960) 136–143.

BLACKMAN, R. B. (1964): "Methods of Orbit Refinement." *Bell System Tech. J.*, **43** (1964), 885–909.

BLACKMAN, R. B., BODE, H. W., SHANNON, C. E. (1948): "Data Smoothing and Prediction in Fire-Control Systems." *Summary Technical Report of Division 7, NDRC*, Vol. 1, pp. 71–160. Reprinted as *Report Series, No. 13, MGC 12/1* (August 15, 1948), National Military Establishment, Research and Development Board.

BLACKMAN, R. B., TUKEY, J. W. (1959): *The Measurement of Power Spectra from the Point of View of Communications Engineering.* (Dover, 1959)

BODE, H. W. (1945): *Network Analysis and Feedback Amplifier Design.* (Van Nostrand, 1945)

BODE, H. W., SHANNON, C. E. (1950): "A Simplified Derivation of Linear Least Squares Smoothing and Prediction Theory." *Proc. IRE*, **38** (1950) 417–425.

BOX, G. E. P. (1954): "Some Theorems on Quadratic Forms Applied in the Study of Analysis of Variance Problems." *Ann. Math. Stat.*, **25** (1954) 290–302.

BROUWER, D., CLEMENCE, G. M. (1961): *Methods of Celestial Mechanics.* (Academic Press, 1961), Chapter IX.

BURFORD, T. M. (1958): "Nonstationary Velocity Estimation." *Bell System Tech. J.*, **37** (1958) 1009–1021.

CLAUS, A. J., BLACKMAN, R. B., HALLINE, E. G., RIDGWAY, W. C., III (1963): "Orbit Determination and Prediction, and Computer Programs." *Bell System Tech. J.*, **42** (1963) 1357–1382.

CROOKS, J. W. Jr. (1948): "Guidance System for the MX-774 Missile." *Report No. ZM7-011, Consolidated Vultee Aircraft Corp.*, August 18, 1948.

DARLINGTON, S. (1950): "Vertical Velocity Computer Data Smoothing Possibilities." *Technical memorandum written for Sandia Corporation*, March 31, 1950.

DARLINGTON, S. (1954): Classified document.

DARLINGTON, S. (1958): "Linear Least Squares Smoothing and Prediction with Applications." *Bell System Tech. J.*, **37** (1958) 1221–1294.

EVANS, M. J., MYERS, G. H., TIMKO, J. W. (1963): "Command Guidance of Telstar Launch Vehicle." *Bell System Tech. J.*, **42** (1963) 2153–2168.

FOX, C. (1950): *An Introduction to the Calculus of Variations.* (Oxford, 1950)

FRIEDLAND, B. (1958): "Least Squares Filtering and Prediction of Nonstationary Sampled Data." *Information and Control*, **1** (1958) 297–313.

GRENANDER, U., ROSENBLATT, M. (1957): *Statistical Analysis of Stationary Time Series.* (Wiley, 1957)

JAMES, H. M., NICHOLS, N. B., PHILLIPS, R. S. (1947): *Theory of Servomechanisms.* MIT Radiation Laboratory Series, Vol. 25 (McGraw-Hill, 1947).

JEFFREYS, H. (1948): *Theory of Probability.* (2nd edition, Oxford, 1948)

JENKINS, G. M. (1961): "General Considerations in the Analysis of Spectra." *Technometrics*, **3** (1961) 133–166.

JENKINS, G. M. (1963): "An Example of the Estimation of a Linear Open Loop Transfer Function." *Technometrics*, **5** (1963) 227–245.

KALLMANN, H. E. (1940): "Transversal Filters." *Proc. IRE*, **28** (1940) 302–310.

KOLMOGOROV, A. (1941): "Interpolation und Extrapolation von Stationaren Zufalligen Folgen, "*Bull. Acad. Sci. (URSS) Ser. Math.*, **5** (1941) 3–14.

LANING, J. H., Jr., BATTIN, R. H. (1955): "An Application of Analog Computers to the Statistical Analysis of Time Variable Networks." *IRE Trans. on Circuit Theory*, **CT-2** (1955) 44–49.

LANING, J. H., Jr., BATTIN, R. H. (1956): *Random Processes in Automatic Controls.* (McGraw-Hill, 1956)

LEVINE, N. (1961): "Increasing the Flexibility of Recursive Least Squares Data Smoothing." *Bell System Tech. J.*, **40** (1961) 821–840.

LIGHTHILL, M. J. (1958): *An Introduction to Fourier Analysis and Generalized Functions.* (Cambridge, 1958)

LING, D. P. (1958): "Radio-Inertial Guidance." Chapter 25 in *Space Technology*, edited by H. S. Seifert. (Wiley, 1959)

LOVELL, C. A. (1944): "A Long-Range, High-Angle Electrical Antiaircraft Director." (Final Report on T-10), *NDCrc-127, Report to the Services 80*, Bell Telephone Laboratories, Incorporated, June 24, 1944.

MUSA, J. D. (1963): "Discrete Smoothing Filters for Correlated Noise." *Bell Systems Tech. J.*, **42** (1963) 2121–2151.

Myers, G. H., Thompson, T. H. (1961): "Guidance of Tiros I." *J. Am. Rocket Soc.*, **31** (1961) 636–640.

Norton, E. L. (1945): "Antiaircraft Director T-15-E1." *OEMsr-353, Report to the Services 98*, Bell Telephone Laboratories, Incorporated, July 30, 1945.

O'Donohue, J. P. (1962): A Note on Using Cascaded Simple Averages for Obtaining Acceleration Information. *IRE Trans. on Circuit Theory*, **CT-9** (June, 1962) 187.

O'Neill, E. L. (1963): *Introduction to Statistical Optics.* (Addison-Wesley, 1963)

Papoulis, A. (1962): *Fourier Integral and Its Applications.* (McGraw-Hill, 1962)

Parzen, E. (1957): "On Consistent Estimates of the Spectrum of a Stationary Time Series." *Ann. Math. Stat.* **28** (1957) 329–348.

Parzen, E. (1961a): "Mathematical Considerations in the Estimation of Spectra." *Technometrics*, **3** (1961) 167–190.

Parzen, E. (1961b): "An Approach to Time Series Analysis." *Ann. Math. Statist.*, **32** (1961) 951–989.

Parzen, E. (1962): *Stochastic Processes.* (Holden-Day, 1962)

Perron, O. (1913): *Die Lehre von den Ketten-brücken.* (Teubner, 1913)

Phillips, R. S., Weiss, P. R. (1944): "Theoretical Calculation of Best Smoothing of Position Data for Gunnery Prediction." *MIT Radiation Laboratory Report No. 532*, February, 1944.

Satterthwaite, F. E. (1941): "Synthesis of Variance." *Psychometrika*, **6** (1941) 309–316.

Schwarz, L. (1950): *Théorie des Distributions.* (Hermann et Cie, Paris, 1950, 2 volumes)

Sears, F. W. (1949): *Optics.* (Addison-Wesley, 1949)

Stewart, R. M., Parks, R. J. (1957): "Degenerate Solutions of an Algebraic Approach to the Multiple-Input Filter Design Problem," *IRE Trans. on Circuit Theory*, **CT-4** (1957) 10 14.

Truxall, J. G. (1955): *Automatic Feedback System Synthesis.* (McGraw-Hill, 1955)

Weinstock, R. (1952): *Calculus of Variations.* (McGraw-Hill, 1952)

Welch, P. D. (1961): "A Direct Digital Method of Power Spectrum Estimation." *I. B. M. J. Research Develop.*, **5** (April, 1961) 141–156.

Western Electric Co., Inc. (1943): "Antiaircraft Director T-15," *OEMsr-353, Report to the Services 62*, August, 1943.

Wiener, N. (1942): "The Extrapolation, Interpolation, and Smoothing of Stationary Time Series." *OSRD 370, Report to the Services 19*, Research Project DIC-6037, MIT February 1, 1942.

Wiener, N. (1949): *The Extrapolation, Interpolation, and Smoothing of Stationary Time Series.* (Wiley, 1949) Includes Levinson (1946, 1947)

Zadeh, L. A. (1950a): "Frequency Analysis of Variable Networks." *Proc. IRE*, **38** (1950) 291–299.

Zadeh, L. A. (1961): "Time-Varying Networks," *I. Proc. IRE*, **49** (1961) 1488–1503.

Zadeh, L. A., Ragazzini, J. R. (1950): "An Extension of Wiener's Theory of Prediction." *J. Appl. Phys.*, **21** (1950) 645–655.

SOME ADDITIONAL LITERATURE

BATTIN, R. H. (1962): "A Statistical Optimizing Procedure for Space Flight." *J. Am. Rocket Soc.*, **32** (November, 1962) 1681–1696.

BENDAT, J. S. (1956): "A General Theory of Linear Prediction and Filtering." *J. Soc. Ind. Appl. Math.*, **4** (1956) 131–151.

BENDAT, J. S. (1957b): "Exact Integral Equation Solutions and Synthesis for a Large Class of Optimum Time Variable Linear Filters." *IRE Trans. on Inform. Theory*, **IT-3** (1957) 71–80.

BENNETT, W. R. (1956): "Methods of Solving Noise Problems." *Proc. IRE*, **44** (1956) 609–638.

BLUM, M. (1957a): "Fixed Memory Least Squares Filters Using Recursion Methods." *IRE Trans. on Inform. Theory*, **IT-3** (1957) 178–182.

BLUM, M. (1957b): "On the Mean Square Noise Power of an Optimum Linear Discrete Filter Operating on Polynomial Plus White Noise Input." *IRE Trans. on Inform. Theory*, **IT-3** (1957) 225–231.

BOOTON, R. C., JR. (1952): "An Optimization Theory for Time-Varying Linear Systems with Nonstationary Statistical Inputs." *Proc. IRE*, **40** (1952) 977–981.

BROWN, W. M. (1963): "Sampling with Random Jitter." *J. Soc. Ind. Appl. Math.*, **11** (1963) 460–473.

CHESSIN, P. L. (1955): "A Bibliography on Noise." *IRE Trans. on Inform. Theory* **IT-1** (1955) 15–31.

DARLINGTON, S. (1959): "Nonstationary Smoothing and Prediction Using Network Theory Concepts." *IRE Trans. on Circuit Theory*, **CT-6** (1959) 1–13.

DAVENPORT, W. L. Jr., ROOT, W. L. (1958): *Random Signals and Noise.* (McGraw-Hill, 1958)

DAVIS, R. C. (1952): "On the Theory of Prediction of Non-stationary Stochastic Processes." *J. Appl. Phys.*, **23** (1952) 1047–1053.

FREEMAN, J. J. (1958): *Principles of Noise.* (Wiley, 1958)

FRIEDLAND, B. (1957): "A Technique for the Analysis of Time-Varying Sampled Data Systems." *Trans. Am. Inst. Elec. Engrs.*, **75**, pt. 2 (1957) 407–414.

GOODMAN, N. R. (1957): "On the Joint Estimation of the Spectrum, Cospectrum, and Quadrature Spectrum of a Two-Dimensional Stationary Gaussian Process." *Scientific Paper No. 10*, Engineering Statistics Laboratory, New York University. Also Ph.D. Thesis, Princeton University.

JOHNSON, K. R. (1956): "Optimum Linear Discrete Filtering of Signals Containing a Non-Random Component." *IRE Trans. on Inform. Theory*, **IT-2** (1956) 49–55.

JURY, E. I. (1958): *Sampled-Data Control Systems.* (Wiley, 1958)

KALMAN, R. E. (1960): "A New Approach to Linear Filtering and Prediction Problems." *J. Basic Engineering, Trans. Am. Soc. Mech. Engrs.*, **82D** (March, 1960) 35–45.

LAWSON, J. L., UHLENBECK, G. E. (1950): *Threshold Signals.* MIT Radiation Laboratory Series, Vol. 24. (McGraw-Hill, 1950)

LEES, A. B. (1956): "Interpolation and Extrapolation of Sampled Data." *IRE Trans. on Inform. Theory*, **IT-2** (1956) 12–17.

LEVINSON, N. (1946): "The Wiener RMS Error Criterion in Filter Design and Prediction." *J. Math. Phys.*, **25** (1946) 261–278.

LEVINSON, N. (1947): "A Heuristic Exposition of Wiener's Mathematical Theory of Prediction and Filtering." *J. Math. Phys.*, **26** (1947) 110–119.
(Note: These two articles by Levinson are reproduced in Wiener, 1949.)

LLOYD, S. P., McMILLAN, B. (1956): "Linear Least Squares Filtering and Prediction of Sampled Signals." *Proceedings of the Symposium on Modern Network Synthesis.* Microwave Research Institute Symposia Series, **5** (1956) 221–247.

MacCOLL, L. A. (1945): *Fundamental Theory of Servomechanisms.* (Van Nostrand, 1945)

MILLER, K. S., ZADEH, L. A. (1956): "Solution of an Integral Equation Occurring in the Theories of Prediction and Detection." *IRE Trans. on Inform. Theory*, **IT-2** (1956) 72–75.

MURTHY, V. K. (1963): Estimation of the Cross-Spectrum. *Ann. Math. Stat.*, **34** (1963) 1012–1021.

PARZEN, E. (1960a): *Modern Probability Theory and its Applications.* (Wiley, 1960)

PARZEN, E. (1960b): "A New Approach to the Synthesis of Optimal Smoothing and Prediction Systems." *Technical Report No. 34*, July 15, 1960. Department of Statistics, Stanford University. (To be published in the *Proceedings of a Symposium on Optimization*, R. Bellman, editor.)

PARZEN, E., HEXT, G. R. (1961): "A Bibliography of American Publications on Stochastic Processes and Time Series Analysis Published in the Years 1900–1959." (Preliminary Report.) *Stanford University Technical Report, 1961.* (To be included in a bibliography on Time Series and Stochastic Processes being compiled by the International Statistical Institute.)

PIERCE, J. R. (1956): "Physical Sources of Noise." *Proc. IRE*, **44** (1956) 601–608.

PRESS, H., HOUBOLT, J. C. (1955): "Some Applications of Generalized Harmonic Analysis to Gust Loads on Airplanes." *J. Aeronautical Sci.*, **22** (1955) 17–26.

PRIESTLY, M. B. (1962): "Basic Considerations in the Estimation of Spectra." *Technometrics*, **4** (1962) 551–564.

RAGAZZINI, J. R., FRANKLIN, G. F. (1958): *Sampled-Data Control Systems.* (McGraw-Hill, 1958)

RICE, S. O. (1944, 1945): "Mathematical Analysis of Random Noise." *Bell System Tech. J.*, **23** (1944) 282–332, and **24** (1945) 46–156.

SALZER, J. M. (1954): "Frequency Analysis of Digital Computers Operating in Real Time." *Proc. IRE*, **42** (1954) 457–466.

SHAPIRO, H. S., and SILVERMAN, R. A. (1960): "Alias-Free Sampling of Random Noise." *J. Soc. Ind. Appl. Math.*, **8** (1960) 225–248.

SOLODOVNIKOV, V. V. (1952): *Introduction to the Statistical Dynamics of Automatic Control Systems.* (Dover, 1960.) (Translation of first Russian edition published in 1952)

SPETNER, L. M. (1954): "Errors in Power Spectra due to Finite Sample." *J. Appl. Phys.*, **25** (1954) 653–659.

STUMPERS, F. L. H. M. (1953–1960): "A Bibliography of Information Theory." *IRE Trans. on Inform. Theory*, **PGIT-2** (Nov. 1953), **IT-1** (Sept. 1955) 31–47, **IT-3** (June 1957) 150–166, **IT-6** (March 1960) 25–51.

SWERLING, P. (1958): "A Proposed Stagewise Differential Correction Procedure for Satellite Tracking and Prediction." *Rand Corporation Report P-1292*, January 8, 1958.

SWERLING, P. (1959): "First Order Error Propagation in a Stagewise Smoothing Procedure for Satellite Observations. *J. of Astronautical Sciences*." **6**, No. 3 (Autumn, 1959) 46–52.

SWERLING, P. (1963): 'Comment on "A Statistical Optimizing Procedure for Space Flight."' *J. Am. Inst. of Aeronautics and Astronautics*, **1** (August, 1963) 1968.

TOU, J. T. (1959): *Digital and Sampled-Data Control Systems*. (McGraw-Hill, 1959)

TUKEY, J. W. (1949): "The Sampling Theory of Power Spectrum Estimates." *Symposium on Applications of Autocorrelation Analysis to Physical Problems*, Woods Hole, June 13, 1949, NAVEXOS-P-735, Office of Naval Research.

TUKEY, J. W. (1959): "An Introduction to the Measurement of Spectra." *Probability and Statistics*, U. Grenander, editor. (Wiley, 1959, pp. 300–330.)

TUKEY, J. W. (1961): "Emphasizing the Connection between Analysis of Variance and Spectrum Analysis." *Technometrics*, **3** (1961) 191–219.

WONNACOTT, T. A. (1961): "Spectral Analysis Combining a Bartlett Window with an Associated Inner Window." *Technometrics*, **3** (1961) 235–243.

ZADEH, L. A. (1950b): "The Determination of the Impulse Response of Variable Networks." *J. Appl. Phys.*, **21** (1950) 642–645.

ZADEH, L. A. (1950c): "Correlation Functions and Power Spectra in Variable Networks." *Proc. IRE*, **38** (1950) 1342–1345.

ZADEH, L. A. (1952a): "Optimum Filters for the Detection of Signals in Noise." *Proc. IRE*, **40** (1952) 1223–1231.

ZADEH, L. A. (1952b): "Analysis of Sampled-Data Systems." *Trans. Am. Inst. Elec. Engrs.*, **71**, pt. 2 (1952) 225–234.

APPENDIX A

LANING AND BATTIN'S METHOD

The particular solution of an ordinary linear differential equation of the form

$$L\{U\} = V, \tag{A-1}$$

where

$$L\{U\} \equiv \sum_{i=0}^{n} a_i(t) \frac{d^i U}{dt^i} \tag{A-2}$$

$$V \equiv K\{E\} \tag{A-3}$$

$$K\{E\} \equiv \sum_{j=0}^{m} b_j(t) \frac{d^j E}{dt^j} \tag{A-4}$$

may be expressed in the form

$$U(t) = \int_{-\infty}^{\infty} I(t;\lambda) E(\lambda) \, d\lambda$$

from which it is obvious that $I(t;\xi)$ is the particular solution of Eq. (A-1) when $E(t) = \delta(t - \xi)$. The impulse response $I(t;\lambda)$ may be determined by the use of a general purpose analog computer, but only for discrete values of λ. It is possible, then, to construct a table of the form shown in Fig. 1.1 and from this table to construct the weighting function $W(\tau;t)$ for equispaced discrete values of τ and t.

However, it was noted by Laning and Battin (1955) that a general purpose analog computer may also be used to determine the weighting function $W(\tau;t)$ directly for any continuous range of τ starting at $\tau = 0$ and for any discrete value of t. This possibility rests upon the fact that $W(\tau;t^*)$ is given by the explicit differential equation

$$W(\tau;t^*) = K^*\{H(\tau;t^*)\}, \tag{A-5}$$

where

$$K^*\{H(\tau;t^*)\} \equiv \sum_{j=0}^{m} \frac{d^j}{d\tau^j} \{b_j(t^* - \tau) H(\tau;t^*)\}, \tag{A-6}$$

and $H(\tau;t^*)$ is the particular solution of the implicit differential equation

$$L^*\{H(\tau;t^*)\} = \delta(\tau), \tag{A-7}$$

where

$$L^*\{H(\tau;t^*)\} \equiv \sum_{i=0}^{n} \frac{d^i}{d\tau^i} \{a_i(t^* - \tau) H(\tau;t^*)\}. \tag{A-8}$$

171

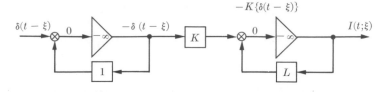

FIG. A.1. Representation of the determination of the impulse response of a variable linear scheme.

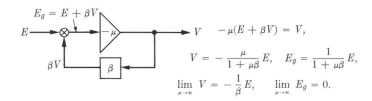

FIG. A.2. Transmission through a hypothetical infinite-gain amplifier with feedback.

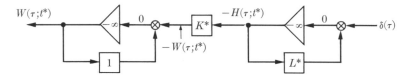

FIG. A.3. Representation of the determination of the weighting function of a variable linear scheme according to Laning and Battin.

Figure A.1 is a schematic representation of Eqs. (A–1)–(A–4), using a symbolism based on Fig. A.2. Similarly, Fig. A.3 is a schematic representation of Eqs. (A–5)–(A–8.) These representations are intended only as mnemonic devices or as analytical aids. As analytical aids, they were used to construct their discrete versions, Figs. 1.3 and 1.4.

If Eqs. (A–5)–(A–8) are to be actually programmed on a general purpose analog computer, they must first be turned into integral equations with a step-function excitation.

APPENDIX B

NETWORK CONFIGURATIONS

Fig. B.1. $Y(p) = \dfrac{1}{1 + b_1 p}$ $(b_1 > 0)$.

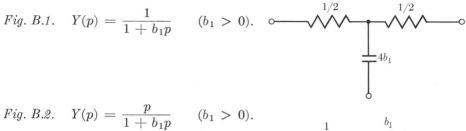

Fig. B.2. $Y(p) = \dfrac{p}{1 + b_1 p}$ $(b_1 > 0)$.

The next four configurations are for

$$Y(p) = \frac{1 + a_1 p + a_2 p^2}{1 + b_1 p} \qquad (a_1, a_2, b_1 > 0).$$

Fig. B.3:   No other restrictions on a_1, a_2, b_1.   *Fig. B.4:* $b_1(a_1 - b_1) \geq a_2$.

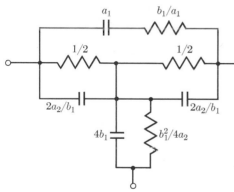
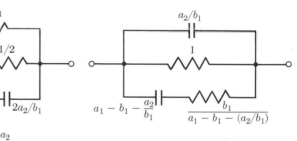

Fig. B.5: $b_1(a_1 - b_1) \leq a_2$,   *Fig. B.6:* $b_1(a_1 - b_1) \leq a_2$,

and $b_1 \leq a_1$.   and $b_1 \geq (a_2/a_1)$.

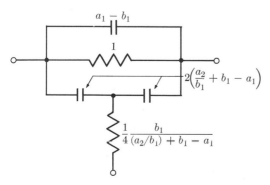
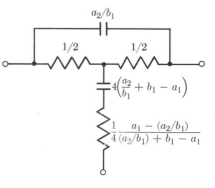

The next two configurations are for

$$Y(p) = \frac{1 + a_1 p}{1 + b_1 p} \qquad (a_1, b_1 > 0).$$

Fig. B.7: $a_1 > b_1$.   *Fig. B.8: $a_1 < b_1$.*

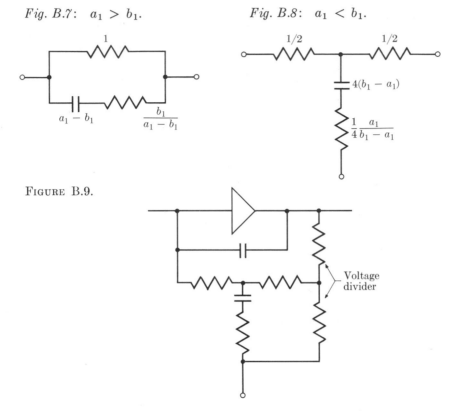

FIGURE B.9.

Each of these configurations, except the first three, may be recast by standard circuit transformation techniques. However, the forms given here usually provide the most convenient element values.

Awkward element values may often be avoided by using voltage-dividers. In Fig. B.6, for example, if a_1 is very nearly as large as $(a_2/b_1) + b_1$, the shunt branch would call for a very large resistance. This may be avoided by using a voltage-divider as suggested in Fig. B.9.

APPENDIX C

NOISE POWER INTEGRALS

If

$$I_n = \frac{2}{\pi} \int_0^\infty |S_n(i\omega)|^2 \, d\omega,$$

where

$$S_n(p) = \frac{1 + A_1 p + \cdots + A_{n-1} p^{n-1}}{1 + B_1 p + \cdots + B_n p^n},$$

then

$$I_1 = \frac{1}{B_1}, \qquad I_2 = \frac{B_2 + A_1^2}{B_1 B_2}, \qquad I_3 = \frac{B_3(B_2 + A_1^2 - 2A_2) + B_1 A_2^2}{B_3(B_1 B_2 - B_3)},$$

$$I_4 = \{B_4[B_3(B_2 + A_1^2 - 2A_2) + B_1(A_2^2 - B_4 - 2A_1 A_3)]$$

$$+ A_3^2(B_1 B_2 - B_3)\} / \{B_4[B_3(B_1 B_2 - B_3) - B_1^2 B_4]\}.$$

Higher-order formulas, in a different notation, are given in the appendix in James, Nichols, and Phillips (1947). A somewhat simpler derivation and formulation of the higher order formulas is given in Appendix E in Laning and Battin (1956).

APPENDIX D

ALGEBRAIC POWER SUMS

Explicit formulas for $S_{nr} = \sum_{m=0}^{n} m^r$, where $r = 0, 1, 2, \ldots$, may be derived by observing that S_{nr} is the rth moment of $W(\tau) = \delta(\tau) + \delta(\tau - 1) + \delta(\tau - 2) + \cdots + \delta(\tau - n)$. The Fourier transform of $W(\tau)$ is

$$Y(p) = 1 + e^{-p} + e^{-2p} + \cdots + e^{-np} = \frac{1 - e^{-(n+1)p}}{1 - e^{-p}}.$$

Expanding the numerator and denominator of $Y(p)$ separately into power series in p, we get

$$Y(p) = \frac{(n+1) - [(n+1)^2/n!]p + [(n+1)^3/3!]p^2 - [(n+1)^4/4!]p^3 + \cdots}{1 - (1/2!)p + (1/3!)p^2 - (1/4!)p^3 + \cdots}.$$

Since this must be equal to

$$S_{n0} - S_{n1}p + \frac{S_{n2}}{2!}p^2 - \frac{S_{n3}}{3!}p^3 + \cdots,$$

we get equations like

$$S_{n0} = n + 1, \qquad S_{n1} + \frac{1}{2}S_{n0} = \frac{(n+1)^2}{2},$$

$$S_{n2} + S_{n1} + \frac{1}{3}S_{n0} = \frac{(n+1)^3}{3}, \qquad S_{n3} + \frac{3}{2}S_{n2} + S_{n1} + \frac{1}{4}S_{n0} = \frac{(n+1)^4}{4},$$

or, in general,

$$S_{nr} = \frac{(n+1)^{r+1}}{r+1} - (r!) \sum_{m=0}^{r-1} \frac{S_{nm}}{m!(r-m+1)!}.$$

Solving these equations we get

$S_{n0} = n + 1,$

$S_{n1} = \frac{1}{2}n(n + 1),$

$S_{n2} = \frac{1}{6}n(n + 1)(2n + 1),$

$S_{n3} = \frac{1}{4}n^2(n + 1)^2,$

$S_{n4} = \frac{1}{30}n(n + 1)(2n + 1)(3n^2 + 3n - 1),$

$S_{n5} = \frac{1}{12}n^2(n + 1)^2(2n^2 + 2n - 1),$

$S_{n6} = \frac{1}{42}n(n + 1)(2n + 1)(3n^4 + 6n^3 - 3n + 1),$ (Note that there is no n^2

$S_{n7} = \frac{1}{24}n^2(n + 1)^2(3n^4 + 6n^3 - n^2 - 4n + 2),$ term in the last factor).

$S_{n8} = \frac{1}{90}n(n + 1)(2n + 1)(5n^6 + 15n^5 + 5n^4 - 15n^3 - n^2 + 9n - 3),$

$S_{n9} = \frac{1}{20}n^2(n + 1)^2(2n^6 + 6n^5 + n^4 - 8n^3 + n^2 + 6n - 3),$

$S_{n10} = \frac{1}{66}n(n + 1)(2n + 1)(3n^8 + 12n^7 + 8n^6 - 18n^5 - 10n^4 + 24n^3 + 2n^2 - 15n + 5).$

APPENDIX E

DETERMINATION OF OPTIMUM $T_1 : T_2 : T_3$

The weighting function corresponding to differentiation and simple continuous averaging of length T_1 is

$$\frac{\delta(\tau) - \delta(\tau - T_1)}{T_1}.$$

Similarly, the weighting function corresponding to differentiation and simple continuous averaging of length T_2 is

$$\frac{\delta(\tau) - \delta(\tau - T_2)}{T_2} \qquad (T_2 \leq T_1).$$

The convolution of these two weighting functions gives the weighting function

$$\frac{1}{T_1 T_2} [\delta(\tau) - \delta(\tau - T_2) - \delta(\tau - T_1) + \delta(\tau - T_1 - T_2)],$$

which is illustrated in Fig. E.1. The convolution of this weighting function with a rectangular weighting function of length T_3 and area 1, where $T_3 \leq T_2$, gives either of the two basic forms shown in Fig. E.2, depending upon whether $T_3 < T_1 - T_2$ or $T_3 > T_1 - T_2$.

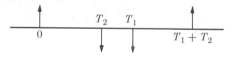

FIGURE E.1.

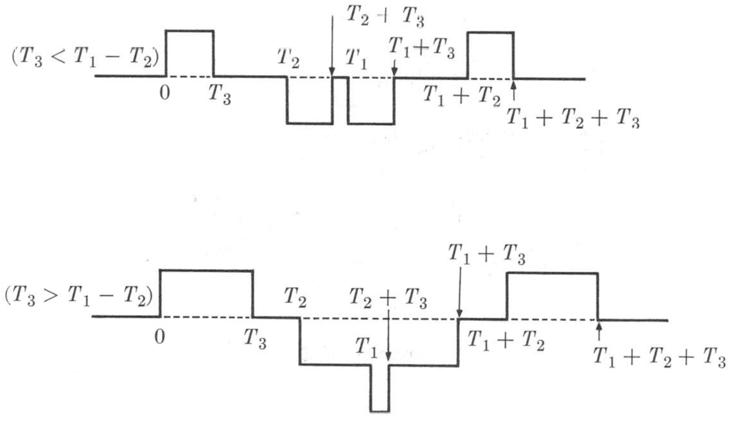

FIGURE E.2.

Hence, the output/input variance ratio is

$$VR = \frac{4}{T_1^2 T_2^2 T_3} \qquad\qquad \text{if } T_3 \leq T_1 - T_2,$$

$$= \frac{2(3T_3 - T_1 + T_2)}{T_1^2 T_2^2 T_3^2} \qquad \text{if } T_3 \geq T_1 - T_2.$$

Introducing the constraint

$$T_1 + T_2 + T_3 = T,$$

and the convenient notation

$$x = T_1/T, \qquad y = T_2/T, \qquad z = T^5 VR,$$

we have

$$z = F_1(x, y) \qquad \text{if } x \geq \tfrac{1}{2},$$
$$= F_2(x, y) \qquad \text{if } x \leq \tfrac{1}{2},$$

where

$$F_1(x, y) = \frac{4}{x^2 y^2 (1 - x - y)},$$

$$F_2(x, y) = \frac{2(3 - 4x - 2y)}{x^2 y^2 (1 - x - y)^2}.$$

The problem now is to determine the point at which z is absolutely minimum within the triangle in the xy-plane (see Fig. E.3) bounded by the lines $x = y$, $x + y = 1$, and $x + 2y = 1$, corresponding to the conditions

$$x \geq y \geq 1 - x - y \geq 0.$$

It is not difficult to show that the point is at $x = \tfrac{1}{2}$, $y = \tfrac{1}{3}$. There, $z = 864$.

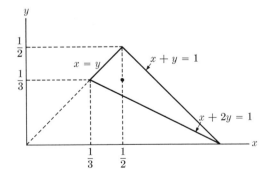

FIGURE E.3.

INDEX